# Managing the Changes in Health Care

The Peirso·

# Managing the Changes in Health Care

AN EXPLANATION AND EXPLORATION OF THE
IMPLICATIONS FOR THE NHS OF
*WORKING FOR PATIENTS*

*Edited by*

## Kevin Teasdale

Wolfe Publishing Limited

Copyright © South Lincolnshire Health Authority, 1992

Published by
Wolfe Publishing Limited
Brook House
2–16 Torrington Place
London WC1E 7LT

Printed by BPCC Hazells Ltd, Aylesbury, England.

ISBN 0 7234 1805 5

For full details of all Wolfe titles please write to
Wolfe Publishing Ltd, Brook House, 2–16 Torrington Place,
London WC1E 7LT, England.

# CONTENTS

# *Preface*

In 1989, the British Government published a White Paper called *Working for Patients*. This was incorporated by Parliament into the 1990 NHS and Community Care Act. It introduced radical changes in the way the National Health Service (NHS) is financed and run. These changes will affect all who work in the service and all those who use it as patients. This book explains the new system in a clear and politically neutral way, so that it can be understood by the interested general reader as well as by the healthcare professional. The book also helps all those who work in the Health Service to think through the effects of the changes upon themselves and upon their areas of responsibility.

*Managing the Changes* has been designed to be used flexibly. It can be read as a source of information and reference; it can be used by an individual as self-teaching material; and it can also be used by groups of NHS staff as discussion or training material.

The first three chapters give an *overview* of how the new arrangements will work, with particular emphasis on *finance* and on *contracts*. Detailed information about the workings of the new system is given here, and sample contract documents are shown in the Appendices. The remaining chapters of the book help the reader to explore the implications for the service of the introduction of *Working for Patients*. With the establishment of a competitive internal market, many hospitals and community units are seeking to adapt *business planning* and *marketing* methods from the world of commerce. *Quality* is a major element of contracts and therefore needs careful analysis at all levels of the service. Because these arrangements are so new, a whole range of different requirements for *information* will become necessary. Finally, because the changes are so sweeping, *managing change* so as to keep stress and disruption to patient care at a minimum will be a top priority for all who work in the NHS.

**Kevin Teasdale**
**Editor**

# *Acknowledgements*

The ideas contained in this book are drawn from many sources. As far as possible, published sources have been acknowledged in the text and in the further reading sections. If any references have been omitted, please accept that this was unintentional; if you contact the publisher, appropriate revisions will be made in future editions.

This book began life as a teaching package produced by a group of senior managers in South Lincolnshire to help staff in their district to understand how *Working for Patients* would affect them locally. It has now been thoroughly re-edited for a wider audience. The Editor takes full responsibility for this revision of the original materials, and for any mistakes or misinterpretations that have arisen therefrom.

Grateful acknowledgement is given to the following people for their original written contributions, or for constructive comments and clarifications: Barry Blakemore, Carolyn Clifton, Mike Frogatt, Martin Gibson, Sheila Gillyett, Jean Jones, Audrey Lathwood and Mid Trent College, Martin Hewings and Pannell Kerr Foster, Brian Mayhew Smith, David Mellor, Chris Pearce, Yvonne Pepperdine, Malcolm Townson, Bob Tucker, and Kevin Turner.

# 1 — The Main Changes: An Overview

---

THIS SECTION IS DESIGNED TO HELP YOU TO:

● *Understand the Key Principles behind the White Paper WORKING FOR PATIENTS*

● *Consider the Main Changes that these Principles will bring to the Health Service*

## The aim of the white paper

The avowed aim of the changes to the National Health Service first announced in the White Paper *Working for Patients* is to raise the performance of all hospitals and GP practices to that of the best. The thinking behind this is that the quality and cost of the service offered to patients vary considerably from one hospital or community unit to another. The Health Service is an enormous organisation, and so it is very difficult to bring about improvements in its services that are consistent across the country. The White Paper has proposed a new way of motivating the service to improve itself – through introducing the principle of competition in an internal market. One aim is to ensure that health service units compete against one another for funds, thus providing a powerful motivator to improve the efficiency and effectiveness of the service.

This new principle of competition is being introduced through five important changes in the way the Health Service is funded and organised:

- Money will follow the patient.
- An internal market of purchasers and providers will be created.
- The market will be regulated by written contracts between purchasers and providers. These contracts will state the quantity, quality, and cost of the health services to be provided.
- Providers will have greater freedom over the way they run their units in order to win and fulfil their contracts.
- New arrangements will be introduced to audit quality of service and value for money.

The remainder of this chapter explores what these changes mean in terms of the day-to-day organisation and running of the service.

## Money will follow the patient

In the past, Health Service funding was 'buildings-led'. This means that where large hospitals were built, large sums of public money were given to support them. The problem with this system was that it took no account of population movements. For example, inner-city areas were heavily populated in the nineteenth century, when many of our larger hospitals were built. In this century, much of the population has moved out to the suburbs, but the money to provide health services for these people has continued to be allocated to the inner-city hospitals. The same problem has affected some seaside areas, where elderly people choose to live in their retirement: the money for their health services has been tied into the hospitals in the areas where they used to live before they retired.

Since the mid-1970s, attempts have been made to reallocate resources to districts with growing local populations. *Working for Patients* will greatly accelerate this process by introducing a funding system which depends totally on the size of the local population, and not upon the size of its hospitals. Census figures will be used to monitor population movements, although they may need to be supplemented from other sources to ensure their accuracy. These population or 'capitation' figures will need to be adjusted or 'weighted' to allow for age and disease factors. This means that funding in some places will have to be increased to allow for a higher than average concentration of elderly people, or of AIDS sufferers, since these groups will make greater demands on health services than others.

Thus, public money for the Health Service will be divided up in a new way to reflect changes in where the population is living. However, the money does not necessarily have to remain there. The principle is that money follows the *patient*, so it all depends on where the patient goes for treatment. For example, if an inner-city hospital can establish a national reputation for quality in some form of specialist treatment, GPs may well wish to send their patients to that hospital rather than to the local one. If this happens, the money for that patient's treatment should go from the district of origin to the hospital which actually has a contract to treat the patient. Therefore, any hospital or other unit that can attract a larger number of patients than before may gain an increase in its income. This is where the motivating factor of competition comes into play.

*Money follows the patient.*

## An internal market of purchasers and providers will be created

Competition will take place through the workings of an internal market for health services. In order to create this market, all parts of the Health Service have been reorganised into purchaser and provider roles.

The *purchasers* have the responsibility for using public money to buy health services on behalf of patients. They will be allocated funds in proportion to the size, health and age distribution of the local population. They will have to assess the healthcare needs of their local population, and then to use the public money allocated to get the best possible deal for their patients. This means that they will have to specify in advance the type, quality, quantity and cost of the services they wish to purchase. They will then negotiate with competing provider units to sign contracts for services at agreed prices. Under the new arrangements, the main purchasers in the internal market are district health authorities and GP fund holders.

### District health authorities

In the past, district health authorities have had overall responsibility for ensuring that the Health Service units in their district provide good quality services. Senior managers at district level joined with general managers from the different units to run the service as a whole. They tended to take a district-wide view, so that, for example, if one hospital was overspending and another was underspending, monies would be transferred to keep the district as a whole on an even keel. It can be argued that this system sheltered inefficient units and provided no incentive for them to become more efficient.

Now district health authorities have a changed function: their primary role is to assess the healthcare needs of the local population and then to purchase health services on their behalf from any service provider who offers good value for money. On the other hand, district health authorities must give up some of the direct control they used to exercise over the units in their district. Health authorities will become smaller. In the past, many had large personnel and finance departments that ran these functions for the whole district. Under the new arrangements, personnel and much internal financial management will be organised separately by each provider unit.

## GP fund holders

Fund holders are larger general practices that have put themselves forward to hold public money and to use it directly to buy services for the patients on their lists. In the past this allocation of money would have been to the district health authority. Under the new arrangements, the agreed budget for a fund holder is deducted from the total sum allocated to the district health authority.

For the fund-holding GPs this represents a radical change in their relationship with hospitals and other provider units. They can now negotiate over quality and price issues from a position of strength, since they actually control some of the funds the providers need to run their services. Fund holders are important to providers because there is no new money in the system – it is simply being divided up in a new way. In the past, providers were sure of their income but now they have to compete for it. Even if fund holders control only 2% of the total allocation for the population of a district, that 2% can mean the difference between recruitment and redundancy in provider units. Because of this, there is a danger that the patients of fund-holding practices will receive better or quicker treatment from hospitals that are particularly anxious to win contracts from fund holders. To try to eliminate the risk of a two-tier service developing, new rules are being put in place that will limit the terms of the contracts purchasers and providers can negotiate. This is an area in which the internal market is externally controlled, in the sense that there are limits on its freedom to operate on purely commercial lines.

## Non-fund-holding GPs

GPs who are not fund holders are *not* purchasers under the new system. They are *providers* of services to patients under the terms of the GP contract, administered by the family health services authorities (FHSAs). However, non-fund-holders can still indirectly influence providers through pressure placed on district health authorities by their FHSAs.

The importance of the role of the GP has been highlighted under the new arrangements. Theoretically, all GPs, whether fund-holding or not, have the freedom to refer their patients to any consultant in the country. Non-fund-holders could make the internal market unworkable if they exercised this power of referral in an arbitrary fashion, since district health authorities would have no control over where the public monies allocated to them were spent. A working compromise appears to have been reached over this issue of clinical freedom. Most GPs have agreed to stay largely within existing referral patterns for the time being, and district health authorities have placed contracts with providers based on these patterns. A limited amount of money has been reserved by district health authorities to pay for extracontractual referrals. Some of this money will be needed to pay providers who give in-patient care to patients who fall ill away from home and who need hospital care immediately. However, some of this money will also be used to pay the costs of individual cases, where GPs choose to make a specialist referral not covered by district contracts.

*Working for Patients* also requires all GPs to justify their prescribing habits when the sums involved exceed what might reasonably be expected for a practice of their size. This scheme for 'indicative drug budgets' is designed to encourage more economical prescribing, without depriving patients of medications which their GPs consider they need. Finally, patients can now change their GP more easily than before, since they no longer need to seek the signature of their existing GP on the application for change.

The *providers* are the units which actually give treatment and care to patients. They may be hospital or community units, and may offer any type of service which meets healthcare needs. Their role is simply to provide their services in ways that are efficient and effective in terms of quality, quantity and cost. A major aim of *Working for Patients* is to bring the pressures of market competition to bear upon provider units, in order to force those units to manage themselves in the most efficient and effective way they can. Under the new arrangements there are three main types of *provider* in the internal market – directly managed units, NHS trusts, and the independent sector.

## Directly managed units (DMUs)

These are NHS hospital and community units where the unit general manager remains accountable to the district health authority. This means that although a directly managed unit has some freedom to organise its own affairs, it ultimately has to obey the orders of the district general manager and of the district health authority. Because of this, many district health authorities in practice retain some responsibility as providers, as well as a main purchasing role. In theory they should keep these two roles quite separate (known for obscure reasons as 'erecting Chinese walls'!). In fact, this introduces another external control into the internal market: it puts the general managers of directly managed units in the difficult position of trying to negotiate with their own bosses over what they consider to be a fair price for the services of their units.

## NHS trusts

These are hospital or community units which manage themselves independently from district health authorities – the 'self-governing' hospitals of the White Paper. In effect they are independent provider units competing with all other providers in the internal market. They can decide for themselves which contracts they will compete for, and can take their own decisions over how they will organise themselves to do this. Thus, whereas in practice there may be pressures on directly managed units not to compete too hard against one another in the same district, such pressures are less likely to operate on NHS trusts. On the other hand, the trusts have to take responsibility for their own decisions, and cannot automatically turn to the district for help if the business side of the service runs into difficulty.

To allow trusts to manage these risks, they are given greater freedom to decide how they will use capital assets such as buildings, land or equipment. For example, if they sell land, they will have a large measure of control over what happens to the funds thus raised. They can also make their own decisions over the terms and conditions of contracts for staff, including those of consultant medical staff. Since staff costs are easily the largest single element in the budget of any unit, this whole area of human resource management will become very important in the business plans of all provider units. These two freedoms, over the disposition of capital assets and over staff contracts, are important factors in influencing managers to view trust status as an attractive option.

## The independent sector

In the past, the non-NHS health care in the United Kingdom was provided mainly in private hospitals, which held contracts with insurance firms. Under the new market arrangements, these private hospitals are now free to compete with DMUs and trusts for contracts placed by health authorities or fund holders. This introduces further competitive pressures into the system, since any contracts placed with the independent sector will reduce the pool of monies available for the other providers.

On the other hand, the competition can work both ways. NHS trusts and directly managed units can compete against private hospitals for contracts from insurance companies. They will need to show that they can meet any such contracts without damaging the agreed quantity and quality of care for NHS patients, but NHS units are likely to be very keen to win contracts for non-NHS patients, since these will bring them new income from outside the existing sources of funding.

## The market will be regulated by written contracts

As in the world of commerce, written contracts will be signed by purchasers and providers for all services. These contracts, or service agreements, will determine how much money providers will receive to run their hospitals and community units. Patients will not 'buy' NHS care directly for themselves: purchasers will agree contracts on their behalf, and will be expected to obtain the best possible deal for the population of their district or GP practice as a whole.

In the early years of contracts, the services required will be little different from those that the hospitals and community units have always provided. However, with an increasing emphasis on health promotion and disease prevention, we can expect to see purchasers diverting money into new types of service in the future.

The mechanism for negotiating contracts will be similar to that used in commerce. Purchasers will publish descriptions of the services they wish to buy (known as service specifications). Providers will tender for these contracts, saying how closely they can match the specification and at what price. Negotiations will then go on until agreement is reached. Price will not be the only factor to determine who will win contracts: the contracts will state how many patients are to be treated, and what quality of care will be provided. In health care, the quality of the service offered will always be a major factor in deciding where to place  contracts. In the early years of the system, the negotiations will be broadly collaborative, as purchasers and providers learn for themselves how the new system works. Their aim will be to get the system up and running, rather than to introduce all the pressures of the market at once. However, competitive pressures on contract negotiations will certainly increase over the years.

## Providers will have greater freedom over the way they run their units

All NHS provider units will need a large measure of freedom to respond to the competitive pressures of the new market. They will increasingly be held directly accountable for the services they provide, rather than for the way they provide those services. In other words, purchasers can control the end product – a service of a specific quantity, quality and cost. However, purchasers can no longer exercise detailed day-to-day control over how a unit organises itself to provide that end product.

Managers in provider units will experience a more entrepreneurial environment than before, with greater opportunities to develop their activities, while facing greater risks if others are more successful in the competition for contracts. Many units are publishing new management arrangements based on clinical directorates. The idea here is that if contracts are being placed for the delivery of particular types of clinical service (surgical, medical, etc.), it makes sense to manage your unit along the same lines as the contracts. Accountability for the delivery of the service then becomes clearer. Also, medical and other professional staff can be brought into the management process, and can learn how their decisions on treatment and care affect the financial position of the unit. Senior managers in provider units will have to determine how much authority they can delegate to clinical directorates, so that they can encourage enterprise without losing control of the overall direction of the unit .

## New arrangements for audit

*Working for Patients* has given new impetus to medical audit. This is the professional review of the quality of medical care undertaken by doctors for doctors. It is a form of peer review, whereby groups of doctors agree to pool data about their clinical decisions for discussion and debate about what constitutes good practice. It includes elements of the research process, but follows action research patterns whereby the people under study take the lead in deciding how to conduct the research and how to act upon the results.

In both the hospital and primary healthcare services, medical audit advisory groups have been established to take the lead in encouraging good practice. A balance has to be struck between confidential professional review and the right of service managers to have access to audit information about the quality of the service. The compromise is that although all consultants and GPs should participate in medically led auditing, medical audit advisory groups are 'semi-detached' from district health authorities and FHSAs. The managers have a right to know whether the medical audit system is in place and working, but have no right of access to detailed information about the work of individual doctors. Only the general results of the audit processes should be made available to non-medical managers.

*Working for Patients* has also introduced an independent body, the Audit Commission, to take responsibility for external *value for money audit* of the NHS. The Audit Commission has provided this service in respect of local authorities in England and Wales, and the extension of its activities to the Health Service is seen as a necessary financial discipline under the new framework.

## Memo Point 1.1

Having read through this chapter, you should now understand the main principles of the White Paper changes. You should also have a basic grasp of how these principles will be turned into practice. They will introduce some of the pressures of competition into the hitherto closed world of the Health Service. With any change will come advantages and disadvantages. Review the chapter, thinking about patient care and the aim of bringing all parts of the service up to the level of the best.

List below at least three possible *advantages* and three possible *disadvantages* of the new system.

There are no right or wrong answers to this question. Your list will represent your immediate reaction to the new arrangements described. As you read the later chapters, try to look for ways in which you can influence what happens in your own work area to build on the advantages and to minimise the disadvantages that you have listed.

## Memo Point 1.2

Many managers will have to take responsibility for explaining the changes which result from the new system to their staff. Planning how you would explain the changes can help you to test out how firmly you understand the basic principles yourself. Take as a starting point the idea that *money will follow the patient*.

How will you explain this to a member of your staff? How will you help that person to understand that this single change leads to the internal market, with contracts and new roles for purchasers and providers? Use the space below to jot down how you would go about the above task.

## Summary Point

Check the objectives at the start of this chapter to see if you are satisfied that you have achieved them. Are you now in a position to answer the questions below? If so, you will be ready to proceed from this basic outline to the more detailed and specific sections which follow.

Is your unit a purchaser or a provider?

Do staff in your area understand the difference?

How will money following the patient affect your unit?

Do you have any responsibility for ensuring your area fulfils its contracts?

What is the purpose of medical audit?

## Further Reading

*Working for Patients*[1] is readable and will be easily available in hospital and public libraries. The other major piece of source material is the *NHS and Community Care Act*[2] itself, which turned the White Paper into legislation. This combined the provisions of *Working for Patients* with those of the community care White Paper, *Caring for People*. For additional reading, Ham's book[3] is a broad overview, while the British Medical Journal publication[4] is a series of articles written from a medical viewpoint and moves on from facts to opinions about how the new system may work. Further background on some of the variations in health care that the new system is designed to remedy is contained in a King's Fund research report.[5] Articles are continually being published that add to the debate about the NHS changes, including some interesting questions about ethics.[6]

[1] Department of Health (1989), *Working for Patients*. HMSO, London.
[2] Department of Health (1990), *The NHS and Community Care Act*. HMSO, London.
[3] Ham, C. (1991), *The New National Health Service*. Radcliffe Medical Press Ltd., Oxford.
[4] British Medical Journal (1989), *The NHS Review – What it Means*. BMJ, London.
[5] Ham, C. (ed.) (1988), *Health Care Variations: Research Report 2*. King's Fund Institute, London.
[6] Johnston, I. and Hunter, D. (1991), Toward moral rearmament, *Health Service Journal*, **101** (5245), 28.

# 2 — *The Finance System*

---

THIS SECTION IS AIMED AT THE
NON-FINANCIAL MANAGER,
IT IS DESIGNED TO HELP YOU TO:

● *Understand How Money Will Flow Through the System*

● *Understand the Effects of Capital Charges on the Way Provider Units are Organised and Run*

## The new basis for funding the NHS

The new system of funding the NHS introduced by *Working for Patients* is based upon four key changes:

● Resident-based funding.
● Money following the patient.
● A system of charging for use of capital.
● Provider units gaining income from contracts.

All staff in the Health Service need to have a basic understanding of this new financial framework, as all will share in the responsibility for ensuring that contracts for services are appropriately set or fulfilled.

## Resident-based funding

As we saw in the first chapter, Health Service funding has in the past been 'hospitals-led', without taking into account changes in the distribution of the population making use of those hospitals. However,

£
£££
£££££
£££££££
£££££££££
£££££££££££
£££££££££££££
£££££££££££££££
**RESIDENT FUNDING**
£££££££££££££££££££
£££££££££££££££££££££
**MONEY FOLLOWING THE PATIENT**
£££££££££££££££££££££££££
£££££££££££££££££££££££££££
**CHARGES FOR THE USE OF CAPITAL ASSETS**
£££££££££££££££££££££££££££££££
£££££££££££££££££££££££££££££££££
£££££££££££££££££££££££££££££££££££
**INCOME WILL COME FROM CONTRACTS**

*The new basis for funding.*

census and other population returns can now be computerised, so it is possible to have very accurate figures for the number of people resident in any one district at any one time. It seems logical therefore to fund the Health Service in each district according to the number of people who will be likely to use its services – this is what 'resident-based funding' or 'capitation funding' means.

The problem with a change to this type of system is that it takes no account of where existing hospitals and other healthcare facilities are sited. Inner-city hospitals, for example, have large numbers of staff on permanent contract employed to deliver services at existing levels, and on the assumption that the funding for these posts was secure. Now those hospitals have to compete to gain enough income from contracts to finance staffing levels which were developed on the basis of the old system of funding. Therefore it is likely that the new system will have to be introduced in a controlled way, if harmful disruption of services to patients is to be avoided.

## Money will follow the patient

You will know by now that money will follow the patient throughout the system – but how will funds move to where the patient needs them, to the point of service delivery?

The Department of Health will allocate public money to the regional health authorities, which are responsible for the strategic planning and monitoring of health care. They will receive an allocation to cover hospital, community and primary healthcare services. They will then 'topslice' their allocations – in other words, they will remove some of the funds before they are redistributed. The topsliced funds will be used by regions to place some contracts directly. For example, contracts for student nurse training will be placed by regions directly with colleges of nursing. Once topslicing is complete, regions will allocate funds to purchasers.

## The purchasers

We have already mentioned two types of purchaser, the district health authorities and general practice fund holders. In addition, the family health services authorities have a limited 'semi-purchaser' role in primary health care, in the sense that they administer the contracts for services with GPs and other primary healthcare providers.

Each purchaser has a duty to buy the best possible health care for the population it serves. 'Best possible' is a balanced calculation based upon an assessment of need and the quantity, quality, and cost of available provision. Purchasers draw up specifications for the services they wish to purchase, and negotiate with potential providers in order to award contracts. Purchasers will have available to them the details of which provider units patients were referred to in the past few years. In the early stages of the internal market, they are under instructions to place contracts with existing providers wherever possible, based on historical activity levels. However, some people may need emergency treatment when away from their own districts, or individuals may need a specialist referral. If their district of residence does not have a contract with the provider unit, the provider will still give treatment and then send an individual bill to the district of residence. District health authorities must therefore keep a sum of money available to meet these 'extracontractual referrals'. It is particularly difficult for them to estimate how much money to set aside for this purpose: on the one hand they must act in a financially responsible way, but on the other hand they do not want to tie up large sums of money which could otherwise be placed with providers in their own districts.

## District health authorities (DHAs)

In the past, DHAs were allocated all the money available from their region to run the hospital and community units in their district. Now DHAs will only have part of the money, with the remainder being allocated to GP fund holders in proportion to the number of patients on their lists. In the early days of the system, DHAs will continue to be the major purchasers of health care for the local population, but theoretically their role could reduce if more general practices apply to become fund holders. There may even be amalgamations between DHAs to increase their purchasing power. DHAs are responsible for researching the healthcare needs of their local population, translating the results into contract specifications, and negotiating these with purchasers to get the best possible deal for local patients.

## GP fund holders

These are larger group practices. Essentially they have two roles, one as providers of primary healthcare services according to the terms of the nationally agreed contract for GPs, administered by the family health services authorities, and the second to purchase hospital and community unit care for the patients on their lists. It is this second role that is described as 'fund-holding'. The funds they hold are allocated by regional health authorities, and are calculated by analysing the patterns of referral to hospital and community units made by GPs in previous years. The provider units give the regions a list of the costs of different types of referral, and these are used to calculate the size of the fund holders' budgets.

These budgets at present cover only a limited range of hospital and community services:

- All out-patient attendances.
- A defined list of 150 in-patient procedures. The list includes most elective surgery by specialty, but not emergency in-patient activity.
- Direct access services such as occupational therapy, physiotherapy, speech therapy, domiciliary visits by hospital consultants, X-ray and pathology as diagnostic procedures but *not* as treatments.

It can be seen therefore that the list excludes maternity services, accident and emergency, psychiatric and mental handicap services. This does not mean, for example, that patients on a fund holder's list may not have babies! It simply means that funding for maternity and other excluded services will be allocated to the district health authority rather than to the fund holder. The fund holder's patients will be covered by DHA contracts with units for these excluded services. In the future it is likely that the list of treatments in fund holders' budgets will increase, perhaps including community nursing services, as fund holders become more confident in purchasing health care.

One safeguard for patients and GPs is that fund holders will not be liable for treatment costs for individual patients over £5,000 per year; costs over this amount will automatically be met through DHA contracts. The overall intention therefore is to allow GPs who are in close everyday contact with patients to develop their purchasing role and to make the hospitals and community units more responsive to the needs of patients. Each fund-holding practice will work independently to devise contract specifications and to negotiate these with provider units.

## Family health services authorities (FHSAs)

FHSAs used to be called family practitioner committees. They are responsible for managing pr'mary healthcare services, including services provided by general practitioners. The FHSAs are purchasers in the limited sense that they administer nationally agreed contracts with general practices. GPs are independent doctors who agree to sign contracts with the NHS, with funding based partly on the size of their lists and partly on how they meet nationally specified healthcare targets. District health authorities will be expected to consult with FHSAs to find out the views of non-fund-holding GPs on the types of hospital and community services which should be purchased for the local population. However, FHSAs and non-fund-holding GPs will *not* place contracts directly with hospitals or community units under the present arrangements.

## The providers

The providers are directly managed units, NHS trusts and the independent sector. To gain income they must first study the specifications for services written by DHAs and GP fund holders. If they wish to enter into contracts with them, they must work out the running costs of their services and seek to recover these through negotiations over the price of the contracts. In the early years of the system, purchasers will be under instructions to place contracts as far as possible with existing providers, and at prices which reflect known costs. However, over a period of time competitive pressures will be allowed to enter the system. Thus there is no reason why a provider unit on the borders of another district should not seek to increase its share of referrals and income from the neighbouring district by competing for its contracts against the district's own providers. This competition is more likely to begin with the smaller contracts placed by GP fund holders rather than with those placed by DHAs.

# Capital charges

Capital charges are a new concept which *Working for Patients* has introduced into the Health Service as a way of forcing providers to review the way they use their capital, i.e. buildings, equipment and land. Capital charges should not be confused with 'capital allocations' or 'major capital schemes', which are funds allocated separately by regions and used mainly to finance major new building schemes. The White Paper does not make any changes to these arrangements.

The capital charges described in *Working for Patients* are simply an accounting device, introduced as another way of bringing market pressures into the NHS system. In the past, the only penalty a unit paid for underusing land, buildings, or equipment was the cost of maintenance, heating, or lighting. In the future, each unit will have to include the cost of its capital in the price it sets for its services. So, units which have buildings or equipment sitting idle will end up setting higher prices than those units which make maximum use of their capital. Purchasers will naturally take this into account when they place their contracts.

To understand capital charges you need to think of all NHS buildings, equipment, and land *(capital)* as owned by the whole population of the UK. We elect governments who manage this capital on our behalf. The Government, through the regional health authorities, loans the buildings, equipment, and land to Health Service units. Nothing is loaned free however – the units pay an interest charge of 6% for the loan of the capital. Unfortunately, buildings and equipment gradually wear out or get damaged – in accounting terms they 'depreciate'; therefore the Government also charges provider units a fixed fee to cover this. Capital charges are therefore made up of these two elements – interest and depreciation.

NHS trusts have a slightly different system to allow for their greater level of management independence: they have to depreciate their own capital assets and show this in their accounts. They also have to earn a target return of 6% on the value of those assets through contracts. The overall effect should be to introduce the same level of pressure on capital as directly managed units will experience. One major advantage which trusts will have over directly managed units is that they will be able to decide what will happen to any money they can generate by selling land, buildings, or equipment. Directly managed units will not have this freedom from district or regional health authority control.

The actual mechanism for calculating and handling capital charges is complex and best left to professional finance managers, but a simplified explanation is worth having. In theory, regional health authorities collect capital charges from all the provider units in their region. They then add this money to their central government allocation of funds and redistribute it to purchasers to buy health services. The provider units have to set their prices so that they can not only cover the costs of providing the services themselves, but also so that they can recover the capital charges they paid to the region.

The pressure on providers is to be more efficient in their use of capital. They can either aim to increase the number of patients who use their buildings and equipment, by winning more contracts, or they can sell capital assets to reduce the amount of capital charges the region will deduct. The competitive pressures are increased by the fact that the independent sector can also tender for contracts. If a private hospital wins a contract from an NHS purchaser, the contract price will probably include at least part of the money collected by the region as capital charges. In other words, the capital charges will leak out of the previously closed NHS system into the independent sector.

It has already been said that the internal market is an 'artificial' market: capital charges are an 'artificial' device, in that they aim in the longer term to force units to manage their capital assets more efficiently than at present. However, the market will need to be managed so that services to patients are improved, not damaged by the new competitive pressures. Therefore it is intended that initially the introduction of capital charges will have a neutral effect; it will therefore seem as if money is being taken away with one hand and given back with the other! The point to remember is that in the longer term the system will increase the pressures on provider units, forcing them to be as efficient as possible with use of capital.

## Memo Point 2.1

To check for yourself whether you know the main facts explained in this chapter, complete the following multiple-choice questions. The correct answers are given at the end of the chapter.

### A. What does resident-based funding mean?

1. Providers are funded according to the number of residents in their district.
2. Purchasers are funded according to the number of residents in their district.
3. Hospitals are funded according to how much residents in the district use them.

### B. Which of the following are providers?

1. Directly managed units.
2. District health authorities.
3. Family health services authorities.
4. GP fund holders.
5. NHS trusts.
6. Private hospitals.

### C. Which of the following are purchasers of general hospital services?

1. Directly managed units.
2. District health authorities.
3. Family health services authorities.

4. GP fund holders.
5. NHS trusts.
6. Private hospitals.

## D. Which items are included in GP fund holders' budgets?

1. Emergency appendicectomy.
2. Elective hysterectomy.
3. Diagnostic X-ray.
4. Day care for the mentally ill.
5. Home visit by a hospital consultant.
6. Radiotherapy for cancer sufferers.

## E. How are capital charges calculated for a directly managed unit?

1. Interest for buildings and land, depreciation for equipment.
2. Replacement costs of buildings, land, and equipment.
3. Interest and depreciation on buildings, land, and equipment.

## F. How do capital charges flow through the system?

1. Providers pay the region, which redistributes to purchasers.
2. Purchasers pay the region, which redistributes to providers.
3. The region pays providers, who redistribute to purchasers.

# Summary Point

This chapter has described how the new financial framework will begin to bring competitive pressures to bear upon providers. The aim is to make them become more efficient and effective in the provision of their services. Contracts are the means by which the system is set in motion – the way these work is explained in the next chapter.

● Funding to be resident-based, weighted for age and disease.

● Purchaser funds to be shared between DHAs and GP fund holders.

● Capital charges aim to force efficient use of assets.

● No new money in the system.

● Providers under pressure.

## Answers to Memo Point 2.1

A2 : B1, B4, B5, B6 : C2, C4 : D2, D3, D5 : E3 : F1

## Further Reading

For more detailed information about how the new finance system works, a prime source of information is the series of Department of Health Working Papers, of which numbers 1–5 are particularly relevant to this chapter. The NHS Management Executive has also produced an excellent written package with video[6], which has not been commercially published but was circulated to all health authority finance departments. For opinion about the finance system, the articles cited below are a starting point. They deal with capital charges [7-8], and the changing role of health authorities [9-10] including Chinese walls!

[1] Department of Health (1989), Working Paper No. 1: *Self Governing Hospitals*. HMSO, London.
[2] Department of Health (1989), Working Paper No. 2: *Funding and Contracts for Hospital Services*. HMSO, London.
[3] Department of Health (1989), Working Paper No. 3: *Practice Budgets for General Medical Practitioners*. HMSO, London.
[4] Department of Health (1989), Working Paper No. 4: *Indicative Prescribing Budgets for General Medical Practitioners*. HMSO, London.
[5] Department of Health (1989), Working Paper No. 5: *Capital Charges*. HMSO, London.
[6] NHS Management Executive (1990), *Keeping the Balance*. Financial Management Training Initiative, Department of Health, London.
[7] Mellett, H. (1991), Paying for goods that were 'free'. *Health Service Journal*, **100** (5237), pp.18–19.
[8] Stirling, B. (1989), Charging into confusion. *Health Service Journal*, **99** (5158), pp. 818–819.
[9] Ham, C. and Best, G. (1989), Goodbye rubber stamp image. *Health Service Journal*, **99** (5147), pp.482–483.
[10] Catchpole, P. *et al.* (1990), Making sure of Chinese walls. *Health Services Management*, **86** (5), pp.221–223.

# 3 — *Contracts*

---

THIS SECTION IS DESIGNED TO HELP YOU TO:

● *Understand the Three Types of Contracts Which Will Be Used in the NHS.*

● *Study an Actual Contract and Identify its Key Features*

● *Identify Some of the Implications of Contracts For Purchasers and Providers.*

## Contracts

*Collins English Dictionary* (1979) defines 'to contract' as 'to enter into an agreement with (a person, company, etc.) to deliver (goods or services) or to do something on mutually agreed and binding terms, often in writing'. The contracts, or service agreements, used in the NHS are the means by which purchasers and providers agree the quantity, quality, and cost of the health services available to the population of their area.

Purchasers must specify the quantity, quality, and price they are prepared to pay for all the services they are allowed to buy. Providers will have analysed what they can provide in terms of quantity, quality, and the cost to them of this level of provision. The two sides then negotiate with the aim of agreeing a contract. The timespan of the contract may vary, but commonly a '3-year rolling contract' is used. This means that the period of the contract is 3 years, but it is reviewed annually. The price and conditions may be varied with the agreement of both parties. It is a 'rolling' contract in the sense that at each annual review, the parties decide whether to let the contract 'roll on' for another 3 years. The point of this is so that providers will always have 3 years' notice of the withdrawal of a contract, to enable them to slim down their service or to look for new business without sudden and damaging disruption.

## Three types of contract

There are three main types of contract between purchasers and providers in the NHS.

1. *Block contracts*, in which the provider agrees to provide a service described in broad terms. The purchaser will pay the provider the annual price of the contract by instalments. In return, residents from the purchaser's district will have access to the range of healthcare services described in the block contract. This contract is relatively unsophisticated and therefore easy to write. Provided referral patterns and the costs of provider units remain stable, it will work well. Problems will occur where referrals, and therefore clinical activity costs, increase during the timespan of the contract. Under a block contract, a hospital must treat as many patients as GPs refer, regardless of the cost. As a safeguard, some providers have negotiated maximum patient limits beyond which renegotiation of the price will take place.

2. *Cost-and-volume contracts*, in which the provider is paid the contract price by instalments in return for providing a defined service for a specified number of patients. For example, a GP fund holder might negotiate a cost-and-volume contract with a provider unit for orthopaedic surgery. Assume that 100 patients were referred for orthopaedic surgery last year; a cost-and-volume contract might state that the first 80 patients this year will be treated for a total price of £80,000. This sum will be paid by the GP fund holder to the provider unit in 12 monthly instalments. If the unit treats more than 80 patients, the price for each additional case will be £1,200. Thus most cost-and-volume contracts agree a fixed sum for treatment for a minimum number of patients, and a price per case for any additional patients.

From the fund holder's point of view, he is only committing 80% of his budget to one hospital. If he is dissatisfied with the way the hospital receives and treats his patients, he can refer a limited number of people to a different hospital if necessary. He does not have to take up the cost-per-case element of the contract.

From the provider unit's point of view, the contract only guarantees 80% of the funding received last year. However, it does mean that if the demand for orthopaedic services increases, the hospital will gain financially because of the higher cost-per-case charge for treating more than 80 patients. Under a block contract system, the hospital would receive the same amount of money no matter how many patients were referred.

3. *Cost-per-case contracts*, in which the purchaser agrees to pay the

provider a defined price for the treatment of each individual patient. Some fund holders are keen on this type of contract, since they do not have to commit their budget in advance to any provider unit. On the other hand, it is administratively complex. Many provider units will charge a higher price for cost-per-case contracts, to recover administrative costs and to discourage purchasers from making widespread use of this type of arrangement.

## Memo Point 3.1

Different types of contract need to be used in different circumstances. To think through the issues, write down your answers to the following questions, then check them against the commentary overleaf.

1. Which type of contract will be used most frequently in the early years of the new system? Give reasons for your answer:

2. How will the administrative costs of the three types of contract vary?

3. Which types of contract require more accurate forecasting information to set a fair price?

# Commentary on Memo Point 3.1

*Different contracts for different purposes*

## 1. Which type of contract will be used most in the early years of the new system?

In the early years of the system, *block* contracts will predominate. The reason for this is that we do not yet have information systems widely available that can deliver the detailed statistics necessary for forecasting clinical activity, nor for measuring how costs behave when activity rises or falls. This problem is true for purchasers, who may need to band together to set up large-scale research projects to improve their knowledge of disease patterns in the population of their districts. It is true also for providers, who may have at their disposal little more than the basic statistics collected under the minimum data sets required by the Korner Reports (1982). Resource management pilot projects have helped improve the quality of descriptive information available to doctors and managers about clinical activity. However, estimations of the true cost of specific procedures, and the way these costs can vary, is still very unsophisticated and uncertain in many units. By using block contracts, purchasers and providers can effectively sign contracts for existing services without the need for accurate and detailed forecasts about the number of people to be treated.

As has been stated, problems can still occur for providers where referrals increase dramatically from the pattern of previous years, since the contract price is fixed at the start of the year. If a purchaser wishes to reduce the number of patients on the waiting lists for treatments, block contracts appear to be unsuitable. If anything, they give providers an incentive to reduce activity levels rather than to increase them. In practice, clinicians are continuing to make their treatment decisions on strictly clinical grounds, but the pressure not to increase activity dramatically is certainly present.

## 2. How will administrative costs vary?

Invoicing and settlement arrangements will have to be agreed in the contract. The contract will also specify measurements of quantity or quality of service which will have to be collected. The more complex the contract, the more expensive the administrative arrangements will become. Therefore, block contracts will be administratively cheaper than cost-and-volume contracts. An individual cost-per-case contract is not administratively very expensive, but if large numbers of these contracts were needed, they would become very time-consuming and costly to administer, since vast numbers of invoices would need to be raised and tracked by providers.

There is no doubt that the new system will increase the administration costs of the Health Service. On the other hand, it will bring the cost of clinical treatments into the open and will expose variations in those costs. The information the new system will generate will make it possible to forecast and control the costs of health services much more closely, but it will be some time before this information can be relied upon.

### 3. Which contracts require more accurate pricing forecasts?

Both cost-per-case and cost-and-volume contracts require accurate pricing forecasts. The problem for purchasers is to know what happens to their costs if numbers either increase or decrease. There may be some economies of scale in treating more patients for example; on the other hand, there may come a point where additional staff have to be taken on to meet the increased demand and the costing equation will change.

Cost-and-volume contracts are only appropriate where both parties have accurate information that enables them to forecast the numbers of patients and types of case that are likely to be treated under the contract. However, when this information is available, purchasers will seek to use this type of contract because they can monitor more accurately how their funds are being used. It is more feasible for GP fund holders with fully computerised practice lists, than for health authority purchasers at this stage. Providers may be attracted to this type of contract for specialist procedures where there is little competition from other providers, as they can set their prices high without fear of losing demand. They will also have a strong incentive to promote their services and to increase clinical activity, thus reducing waiting lists. On the other hand, where there is a lot of competition, and where information about costs is poor, there are real risks of underfunding with a contract which makes no guarantees of income at the start of the year.

## What does a contract look like?

Each district health authority will set up its own detailed specifications, but most block contracts will follow the general format shown in Appendix B. In devising a contract, it is essential that clinicians, managers, and other healthcare professionals are involved from the start. They are the people best placed to identify the strengths and weaknesses of their areas, and their help will be essential in maintaining and developing the quality and quantity of service provision.

Each contract, no matter which type it is, will probably have two main elements – general conditions and an individual service specification.

● *General conditions* are certain principles and issues which affect all contracts placed by a purchaser. They provide a framework for the ongoing management of the contractual process.

● *An individual service specification* is more detailed than the general conditions document. It describes in detail the type, volume, and quality of the service required by the purchaser and agreed by the provider. Certain clauses from the general conditions are developed in more detail in the service specification. Individual services may be defined in different ways. For example, one fund holder may want one service specification for all types of surgery, whereas another may wish to treat each surgical specialty separately.

In order to understand how contracts will work, it is important to study one for yourself. If you work in the NHS it may be possible for you to study the contract that applies to your specialist area. Most health authorities and units will make these available to people who have a genuine reason for wishing to see them. The contracts with GP fund holders may be seen as more commercially sensitive.

A sample version of a block contract between a district health authority and a directly managed provider unit is given in Appendix B for those who cannot get easy access to one for their own district. It shows the set of general terms and conditions which would apply to all the block contracts negotiated by the purchaser, and a detailed service specification (in these examples it is for gynaecology services and community health services, but others will follow a very similar pattern.) The service specification is a sample only and does not contain detailed activity figures, nor a final agreed price. Nevertheless, it will give readers an idea of the main features of NHS contracts.

# Memo Point 3.2

*General conditions for contracts*

Study the sample set of general conditions shown in Appendix B, or the equivalent conditions for your own district if available. Then find the answers to these five questions:

1. What is the legal status of a service agreement?

2. How long will each agreement last?

3. How will wage and price inflation be dealt with?

4. What happens if there is a dispute over the agreement?

5. How might a contract with an NHS trust differ from this one with a directly managed unit?

# Discussion Point 3.2

## 1. What is the legal status of a service agreement?

Section 1 of Document 1 describes this. The agreement is not legally binding, but both parties are expected to abide by it. The arbitration procedure and lines of accountability within the Health Service should be strong enough generally to enforce this. However, NHS trusts may in future years seek stronger and more binding guarantees in order to safeguard their finances. Contracts with insurance companies for additional work would be cast in legally binding forms.

## 2. How long will each agreement last?

This is described in Section 2 of Document 1. It is a 3-year contract, rolling on 1 year. The details are renegotiated annually.

## 3. How will wage and price inflation be dealt with?

This is described in Sections 9–10 of the document. Purchasers will be told by the Department of Health of the additional monies released annually to meet inflation, as illustrated in this document with an assumption of 6%. However, the unit will only receive 5%, and will be expected to make cost improvements to meet the 1% shortfall. Cost improvements might include measures to reduce the use of bank staff to supplement full-time staff; they might involve measures to improve the insulation of hospital buildings to cut spending on heating, etc.

Some managers will argue that centrally set cost-improvement targets are incompatible with the hands-off competitive pressures of the internal market. For several years now targets have been set annually by the Department of Health, and providers argue that it is not possible to continue indefinitely making cost improvements without affecting the quality or quantity of the services provided. Also, under the competitive conditions of the internal market, cost-improvement targets could seem to be heavy-handed interferences with the running of units. Many providers will argue that they should negotiate freely with purchasers over the price of their services, leaving the competitive process alone to put pressure on them to become more efficient.

### 4. What happens if there is a dispute over the agreement?

This is described in Sections 13–14 of the document. It is expected that most disputes will be settled by negotiation. However, a mechanism by which the regional general manager or the Secretary of State could be called in to arbitrate is theoretically available. Most managers would be extremely reluctant to allow this to happen, and the general manager of a directly managed unit would be in a particularly weak position if entering a dispute with the district general manager, who will be his own immediate manager.

### 5. How might a contract with an NHS trust differ from this one with a directly managed unit?

NHS trusts have greater freedom from management directives from the district health authority than do directly managed units. Trusts are therefore likely to be tougher negotiators. They may try to hold out for more favourable conditions over variations in service, in particular where block contracts are used and they fear increases in clinical activity. Cost improvements may at some stage be agreed directly with the region, rather than with districts. Some of the cooperation agreements in Section 12 on performance monitoring and quality may be untenable in relation to a trust. Section 17 on work undertaken for other purchasers could not apply to a trust, which is a free agent in the internal market. However, some form of agreement which ensures that one contract does not adversely affect performance in another would be necessary.

## Memo Point 3.3

*The detailed service specification*

If you work in an NHS provider unit, try to see a copy of the detailed service specification that applies to your own area. If this is not possible, refer to Documents 2 or 3 in Appendix B, which give an imaginary sample specification for gynaecology services and community health services. Remember that each main specialty will probably have a similar detailed specification to be read alongside the general conditions shown as Document 1. The form of these specifications will probably follow a list of headings similar to those shown in Appendix B, even if they refer to specialties as different as mental handicap or health visiting services. The general principles are exactly the same, despite the differences in detail.

Imagine you are the general manager of the provider unit in question. You have just signed the contract for the service described in the specification; now sketch out your *plan of action*.

Study the specification to decide what you will be asking managers, clinicians and other healthcare staff to do, in order to ensure that your unit fulfils its obligations under this contract. Make notes for an outline of your plan in the space below:

# Discussion Point 3.3

The purpose of this exercise was for you to study the specification carefully from the perspective of someone who will be called to account if it is not met. If you work in a provider unit, this may help you to anticipate some of the demands that will be placed upon you by more senior managers. As a potential patient of an NHS provider unit, it may also help you to become more aware of the quality of service you have a right to expect. In the discussion of this Memo Point we will refer to Document 2, but the general points will apply whichever document you chose to study. Your plan of action may have included some of the following elements:

## The consultants

Have a meeting with the consultants and make sure that they fully understand the terms and conditions of the specification. Clearly this will not go down well if you omitted to involve them in the negotiating stages of the contract! However, if they were involved then, it is reasonable to expect them to assist in ensuring that clinical activity is as described in the document. Many units are trying to reorganise internally, using clinical directorates; under these arrangements a consultant may be appointed as director of a specialty, aided by a senior nurse and a business manager. This team will be given considerable freedom to run the specialty, provided that they meet the terms of the contracts. This form of devolution has potential as a way of giving clinicians a greater say in how money is spent, while making them more accountable for the pattern of clinical activity that results.

One area where consultant cooperation will be required is 'tertiary referrals'. Tertiary referrals occur when a patient in one hospital is referred by the hospital consultant to another consultant in a different hospital. The original district health authority will have to agree to this, since some of its purchasing money will have to follow the patient to the new hospital if it does not already have a contract with that hospital. In practice, as with the rest of the system, all should be well provided there is not a dramatic change in the pattern of tertiary referrals from one year to another. However, there is potential scope for disputes over the infringement of clinical freedom in this area.

## Quality

The quality statements are contained in Sections 8 and 9 of the specification. However, Section 12 of the general conditions in Document 1 is also relevant. The general manager will need to ensure that the gynaecology department is organised in such a way that the standards can be met. An internal quality assurance mechanism will be needed to identify any problems at an early stage, so that the contract is not breached. A system of performance review for managers is likely to be used here, to ensure that objectives are delegated in a clear and organised fashion, and then properly monitored.

## Information
Section 10 describes some of the information that must be made available to the purchaser, and further details are to be found in the general conditions in Document 1. Computerised information systems are essential for handling much of these data, and they need to be designed so that the material only needs to be entered once. Database programs are potentially very good at achieving this, since it is usually possible to pull out summarised information in several different forms, depending on what questions the enquirer asks.

However, it is not enough for the unit to provide information for the purchaser. The general manager will want up-to-date analyses of clinical activity and of the real costs of that activity for his own management purposes. This may require new investment in software, which will have to be budgeted for as part of the unit's overall costs.

New admission forms may be needed for all patients, to check precisely where they live. Although most patients will be covered under this block contract, those from other districts will need to be identified separately. The same will hold true for the specified list of treatments for patients of GP fund holders. Systems will have to be set up to collect these data in the first place, and then to ensure that they are entered correctly in the computer database.

## Finance
This is a block contract, and therefore is more straightforward to administer from a financial viewpoint than a cost-and-volume or cost-per-case contract. However, the unit will certainly need to have a qualified financial accountant on site, and this will probably be a department which will increase in size as the corresponding department at the district health authority contracts.

There will have to be a mechanism for checking that the expected sums of money are provided monthly by the purchaser. With other types of contract, a more complex system of invoices will be needed. If the hospital receives tertiary referrals from another hospital, an invoice will need to be sent to the district health authority or fund holder where the patient is resident. Setting up and managing all these systems will be the task of the unit accountant.

## Communication and training
Setting up all these systems will affect everyone involved in providing healthcare services. The general manager will need to ensure that staff actually know what has been agreed by him on their behalf. The quality standards cannot be enforced by managers – they must be willingly accepted and continually worked at by the staff, who have everyday

contact with the patients. Whether you call this 'communication' or 'training' is immaterial. A clear development strategy will be needed, for the unit as a whole and for each department in particular.

## Summary Point

There has been a lot to study in this chapter and it is important to avoid becoming overwhelmed by all the detail. This is why the Memo Points have asked you to think for yourself about the things which really matter in the contractual process.

● Contracts deal with quantity, quality, and price.

● Doctors and managers must communicate to make them work.

● All staff need to know what is expected of them.

● Patients need to know the quality standards and who to complain to if they are not met.

## Further Reading

For additional factual information there is a Working Paper[1] issued by the Department of Health. For opinion, Hughes[2] examines the legal status of NHS trusts and Ham[3] looks at potential conflict between purchasers.

[1] Department of Health (1989), Working Paper No. 2: *Funding and Contracts for Hospital Services*. HMSO, London.
[2] Hughes, D. and Dingwall, R. (1990), What's in a name? *Health Service Journal* **100** (5229), pp.1770–1771.
[3] Ham, C. and Heginbotham, C. (1991), How to make a future champion. *Health Service Journal* **101** (5262), pp.20–21.

## References

Hanks, P. (ed) (1979), *Collins Dictionary of the English Language*. William Collins & Sons, London.
Korner, E. (1982), *Steering Group on Health Services Information: First Report to the Secretary of State*. HMSO, London.

# 4 — *Business Planning*

---

THIS SECTION IS DESIGNED TO HELP YOU TO:

● *Understand the Importance of Business Planning*

● *Begin to Write a Business Plan For Your Own Area*

## Business planning

The division between purchasers and providers of health care is similar to that between customers and manufacturers in industry. Over the years, businesses in the commercial world have evolved ways of planning and organising that have enabled them to respond to the pressures of the competitive environment in which they operate. Therefore if the pressures of the market place are being brought into the NHS, it makes sense for providers to examine the business planning process and see if they can usefully adapt its methods in order to succeed in winning and fulfilling contracts.

In the past, planning in the Health Service has revolved around the strategic plan – attempting to set a programme of aims and objectives for a 10-year period to give overall direction to the service; and the annual programme – setting out the details of how resources will be used to progress towards the strategic aims and objectives over a 2-year period. However, the new environment resulting from *Working for Patients* will demand a more responsive style of organisation and planning. To manage successfully, both purchasers and providers will have to focus their attention on the services their local populations need and want.

The business planning model will need to be adjusted to translate into the NHS. For example, who are the customers of provider units? Are they the patients, or are they the organisations that purchase care on their behalf? For the purposes of this section we will reserve the word 'customer' for the purchasing organisations. The marketing term 'consumer' could therefore be applied to patients, clients, residents, or even visitors.

Units will use business planning in different ways to suit their circumstances. An NHS trust will have to function in ways very similar to a commercial organisation, whereas a directly managed unit may take some planning ideas from business but still retain features of the strategic and annual planning process. Among purchasers, general practices have always made extensive use of business planning ideas.

*Business manager seeks employment, impeccable references.*

## Key Points

In order to create a business plan, a manager will need to find accurate answers to the following questions:

1. How can business planning help us?
2. What are we in business for?
3. How are we doing? How are our competitors doing?
4. How can we improve our service?
5. What must we do to make it all happen?
6. Does the plan as a whole fit together?

The answer to producing a business plan does *not* lie in giving the job to one person – a 'business manager'. Unless staff feel involved in the planning process, they will not be committed to the goals of the organisation. Each unit will need to develop its own corporate identity, and a good way of building this is to adopt a team approach to business planning. The rest of this chapter will take you through the planning process, using the key points shown above.

## How can business planning help us?

There is no single 'right' answer to this question.

An NHS trust can be regarded as a new business that is using this method of planning to gain commitment from its staff, to set up an organisational structure, and to go out and actively compete for contracts in the market place.

The idea of a directly managed unit as a 'new business' is less satisfactory. The district health authority and the unit will cooperate to ensure that the first contracts largely describe the existing service. The unit is unlikely in the first instance to find itself under great pressure to compete for contracts. However, once the contracts are agreed, the business planning process can be used to ensure that managers organise their areas to fulfil the contracts. This could be a first stage in adapting to the competitive pressures the new system can be expected to generate once the setting-up process is complete.

### Teamwork

The preparation of a business plan is not the responsibility of the general manager alone: one of the principles of *Working for Patients* is that the responsibility for decision making will be devolved as far down the organisation as possible. For example, the move towards clinical directorates in many hospitals is an attempt to involve clinicians and healthcare professionals in the planning process. If business planning ideas have something to offer the NHS, then managers at ward or department level may wish to produce business plans for their own areas. The only constraint is that these plans must be compatible with the plan for the unit as a whole. However, ideally the business plan for a provider unit might evolve from the detailed plans made by committed staff at department or ward level.

## What are we in business for?

### The mission statement

This first step is essential for any organisation. The mission statement is a long-term vision of what the organisation is, or is striving to become. It should be specific enough to give direction, but broad enough to allow the business to grow.

The value of defining the mission is not merely in the statement itself, but in the deep understanding of the core purpose of the organisation that the process can generate among all staff. It must be owned, accepted, and understood throughout the organisation.

A good mission statement should:

- Focus more on customer satisfaction than the characteristics of the service provided.
- Recognise opportunities/threats in the environment.
- Reflect essential skills of the organisation.
- Be specific enough to have an impact upon the behaviour of the organisation.
- Be attainable.
- Be flexible.

Two sample mission statements could be as follows:

1. *For a mental handicap unit:* To improve the quality of life of people with a mental handicap by offering and providing an ever-improving, sensitive, and caring service.
2. *For a college of nursing and midwifery:* The college will provide education and training services to an agreed set of quality standards that will meet the changing needs of its valued customers. The staff of the college are its greatest asset, and they will seize every opportunity to expand services and increase the clientele, working towards the achievement of self-governing status at the appropriate time.

## Memo Point 4.1

Having studied the two mission statements, what do you like and dislike about each one?

However, in case you are becoming too critical, the next task in this Memo Point is to draft a mission statement for your own work area!

How would you consult on your mission statement and gain a commitment to it from other members of staff in your area? Can you think of any other ways of producing a mission statement apart from drafting it yourself?

## How are we doing? How are our competitors doing?

At an early stage in the planning process, managers must take stock of their present position – the starting point for planning. Internally the organisation should consider its strengths and weaknesses. Is it meeting the objectives outlined in the mission statement? Where it is, this will identify strengths that can be expanded or built upon; where it is not, this will help identify weaknesses or areas for improvement. Remember that you are thinking now in terms of the competitive environment of the internal market, therefore a strength is not really a strength if all the competing units share it, and a weakness is not a weakness if everyone suffers from it. The purpose of the exercise is to try to identify the strengths and weaknesses specific to your unit or department.

Externally the organisation should consider any threats. These may be developments that you know about from competitors, or they may be changes to the rules under which the market operates. Again you should balance threats with opportunities. Where is new development possible? Do you know of innovative approaches to care which you can use to make your unit more competitive? This process is known as a Strengths, Weaknesses, Opportunities and Threats analysis – a 'SWOT' analysis.

A SWOT analysis will consider the following areas:

## Internal factors
- Which services are we best at?
- Structures of jobs and departments.
- Communications systems, both internal and external.
- Human resources: numbers, skills, and attitudes.
- Financial strengths, reserves, cash flow, margins.
- Reputation within the Health Service and outside.
- Volatility, e.g. staff turnover.
- Marketing ability.
- Match of organisational effort to key aims and objectives.
- Information systems.

## External factors
- Political – can you anticipate any changes in national or local politics which may affect your service?
- Economic – are there economic factors that might affect your ability to meet objectives? These could be factors affecting cash limits in the NHS, or they could be the development of competitors for contracts or for staff in your area.
- Social – have you allowed for changing customer and client expectations?
- Technical – have you allowed for the impact of technology on costs, quality, and range of services?
- Competitive – have you taken into account as far as possible the strengths and weaknesses of any competitors?

# Memo Point 4.2

Undertake a SWOT analysis of your own work area, using the checklist of internal and external factors on the previous page as a general guide.

Strengths

Weaknesses

Opportunities

Threats

# How can we improve our service?

A mission statement and a SWOT analysis are of no value in isolation. The next step in the planning process is to devise a set of *objectives*, based on the SWOT analysis and compatible with the mission statement. These objectives will supply the driving force to the business plan. They are the elements of the plan which need to be handed on through the appraisal process to all your staff.

Objectives should be *RELEVANT, ACHIEVABLE*, and *MEASURABLE*.

## *Sample objectives from a nursing college business plan*

1. To develop the academic relationship between the college and the institution of higher education through obtaining the accreditation of existing courses, the development of new projects, and the establishment of new appointments.
2. To meet the manpower targets set by the regional health authority, and to fulfil the staffing requirements of district health authorities.
3. To balance the college books within the cash limits and, in addition, to achieve a target growth of 0.5% of the total budget through income generation.
4. To develop a counselling service, initially for college students and staff, and then to expand the service to other groups on a self-funding basis.
5. To set up a computerised college information system within 1 year.

# Memo Point 4.3

Review your mission statement and your SWOT analysis, and then draft a set of objectives which will meet the key criteria of being relevant, achievable, and measurable.

## What must we do to achieve the objectives? Does the plan as a whole fit together?

Finding the answers to these questions is the final step in producing the business plan. The objectives must be communicated to other people who will be involved in their achievement. It may be necessary to restructure the organisation of an area, or of a whole unit, in order to achieve the objectives. Further detailed plans will probably be needed to set up information systems, monitor quality, market services, and manage the changes.

You may wish to complete the business plan you have been drafting right now, by adding the detail of how to achieve the objectives. Alternatively, you may prefer to leave this until later, as most of the topics relevant to this stage are covered in more detail in the later chapters of this book.

The final check before you go ahead and implement your plan is to make sure it fits together as a whole. If a unit is encouraging managers at ward or department level to produce business plans, it will certainly be necessary for the senior management group to study all the resulting plans *together*, before agreeing to their implementation.

This phase of the process is often called *portfolio planning*. It involves reviewing a whole range of possible developments, and seeing how one will affect another. Sometimes this will result in a veto on a plan because the manager at one level of the organisation could not foresee that the plan would actually damage a different part of the same organisation. Sometimes portfolio planning will lend unexpected support to plans. For example, one department may have considered buying a piece of equipment, but decided to postpone it because it was very expensive. However, if other areas could also make use of the same equipment it may become a worthwhile immediate investment. Studying the whole portfolio provides a final check before the decision to implement the business plan is taken.

## Summary Point

### Implementing the plan

Having set out the priorities as part of portfolio planning, the manager can begin to allocate tasks and monitor progress. Having worked through this process it is tempting to breathe a sigh of relief and put the plan away in the bottom drawer! However, business plans need constant updating and revision in order to meet changes in the external environment and new priorities within the organisation.

The business plan should be a 'live' document that feeds into other activities such as budgeting, monitoring contracts, marketing, and service development. Hopefully this chapter will have dispelled some of the mystique surrounding business planning. Essentially it is a commonsense process which, if tackled realistically and honestly, can give managers and staff a real sense of direction.

## *Producing a business plan : the main steps*

- Identify your team.
- Produce a mission statement.
- Conduct a SWOT analysis.
- Set detailed objectives.
- Devise an implementation plan.
- Final check: portfolio planning.
- Implement.

# Further Reading

There are many general texts on business planning, but the articles here explore their relevance to Health Service settings. Deffenbaugh[1] questions some of the myths surrounding the process; Moss[2] gives an example of business planning in a clinical directorate, and Elphick[3] shows how a SWOT analysis can help a unit.

[1] Deffenbaugh, J. (1991), Debunking the plans bunkum. *Health Service Journal*, **101** (5252) p. 23.
[2] Moss, T. *et al.* (1990), From department to directorate. *Health Service Journal*, **100** (5219) pp.1390–1391.
[3] Elphick, C. and Dillarstone, P. (1990), Order out of chaos. *Health Service Journal*, **100** (5186) pp. 200–202.

# 5 — *Information Systems*

---

## Useful information

Information is a 'buzz word' at the moment. For some people it is associated with computers, for others it means reams of statistics; yet information is anything which helps us to understand the world around us. For a manager, information is a basic tool of the trade. The manager who is well informed is in a position to exercise control over what is happening, and to plan realistically for the future.

In health care we frequently talk of keeping our patients fully informed, but how often do we succeed? Never! There is no such thing as 'full information'. All information is partial and most will contain inaccuracies. This is not an admission of neglect of duty, it is an admission that systems are not perfect and that we do not know everything.

It is the same for a manager: no manager will ever have 'full information' about an area of work; all decisions are made on the basis of a 'best guess' approach. Having said all this, we still *try* to give our patients the best quality information available. As managers we still *try* to be as well informed as possible. The reason is clear – the better the quality of our information, the more probable it is that our decisions will be correct.

*What makes information 'useful'?*

To be useful, information should be:

● Timely.
● Accurate.
● Understandable.
● Relevant to user needs.
● Cost-effective to produce.
● Available to those authorised to use it.

## Memo Point 5.1

Review the Memo Points of this book that you have worked through so far. Find one page which set a task that forced you to note down information *useful* to you, and then find another which was *not useful*. Compare the two and note down in your own words the reasons why one was useful and the other was not.

## The scale of a healthcare information system

The National Health Service is the largest employer in Europe. It operates on a huge scale, and in order to manage it efficiently, information about all aspects of its functioning is required. The NHS Management Executive requires information on which to base its strategic planning; district health authorities need information to have a rational basis for purchasing; provider units need information to tell them about their income and expenditure. If you are a Health Service manager, you will need information to run your department efficiently and effectively. Sometimes information collected in order to be useful to one person can also be useful to another. Nevertheless, the scale of Health Service activity sometimes threatens to overwhelm even the most sophisticated information system.

For example, a relatively 'small' health district could have a resident population of 300,000 people and a purchasing budget of £70 million.

Average annual activity would be in the region of 50,000 in-patient admissions, 200,000 out-patient attendances, 500,000 community contacts, and well over 1 million primary care contacts. The district might have three or four provider units, with at least as many GP fund holders as purchasers, as well as the district health authority. Those purchasers would need to place contracts with surrounding districts as well as the home district, so there could easily be 30 separate contractual agreements for over 120 specialty elements, and a requirement to monitor each one. Remember, this is just a small district!

The only way of handling such an enormously varied pattern of activity is to computerise. Primary health care is the area that has made the most progress in using computers to generate useful information, although investment in systems for provider units is beginning to improve the position everywhere. The value of a computer is that you can put information into a filing system or database; you can then question the database, and the computer will automatically move the information around and present it in the form you require. This means that one set of information can be used economically to answer many different questions. Where computer systems can be linked one to another, the potential value of what is stored there is increased.

## Information for contracts

Computerisation has made it possible to collect and process information more cost-effectively than ever before. New computerised information systems are being introduced throughout the service, each with a new acronym:

RMI – Resource Management Initiative
PAS – Patient Administration Systems
MAPS – Manpower and Personnel Systems
DISS – District Information Systems

There is a danger that districts and units will spend their money on isolated systems that will supply information in a form which only they can use; this problem was noted in the 1980s, when a committee headed by Baroness Korner issued a number of reports that tried to specify the basic minimum information required to run the NHS. These information requirements were grouped largely by specialty into 'minimum data sets'.

However, the division into purchaser and provider roles, the development of resident-based funding, and the use of contracts means that the Korner minimum data sets will not be sufficient to manage the new system. One of the most difficult problems facing managers at all levels of the Health Service will be to identify their information requirements under a system of funding by contract.

## Information requirements of purchasers and providers

Purchasers will need to collect information about the healthcare needs of their resident population; they will also need to gather information about the plans of GPs, local authorities and other agencies before they can place contracts. Once placed, they will have to operate the payment system for contracts, and will have to be in a position to check the accuracy of invoices and to monitor the overall state of their finances.

Providers will need information to negotiate contracts. They will have to set up systems to collect the basic data required to create invoices and supporting documentation so that they can claim payment from the purchasers. They will need information to keep a check on their overall financial position, and to prepare new business plans for the future.

**Information requirements**

| Purchaser | Provider |
|---|---|
| Places contracts | Negotiates over contracts |
| Pays invoices | Raises invoices |
| Checks provider activity, quality, costs | Supplies supporting data |
| Monitors overall position | Monitors own financial position |

*Busy office.*

# Memo Point 5.2

What happens to the information collected by your work area? Which part of the system does it fit into?

The remainder of this chapter examines in more detail the information requirements described above.

# The purchaser role

For the purposes of this book, the purchaser will be assumed to be a district health authority, but the ideas can be adapted easily to the role of a GP fund holder. The role of the district as a purchaser can be expressed in terms of four main activities.

## Placing contracts

Districts will require information in order to assess the availability of resources against needs. They will have to collect information about population trends in their district; ideally they will want to move towards a shared population register with family health service authorities. They will seek information to enable them to set up a health event database, which will provide information about the local incidence of particular illnesses or events occurring in identified groups in the local population.

They will need to know what providers can offer in terms of costs, waiting times, quality, and service developments for all treatments and operations. They will need information about the referral preferences of all GPs, otherwise they will find themselves having to pay for large numbers of extracontractual referrals. They will have to work closely with community health councils and other consumer groups to collect information about local healthcare preferences.

The information collected by purchasers will have to be kept in a form that complies with the requirements of the Data Protection Act, and must be available only to authorised users.

## Paying invoices

Purchasers will have to have sound administrative systems for paying the invoices they will receive from providers. Each invoice will have to be checked against a contract. Some invoices will be from units outside the district, perhaps where patients needed emergency treatment while on holiday; these will be extracontractual invoices and will need to be individually checked.

Funds will have to be transferred at regular intervals, and detailed accounts of all transactions must be readily available.

## Checking provider activity, quality and costs

All provider units are required to supply on a monthly basis a minimum data set of information specified in their contracts. This is used to monitor the functioning of all contracts. Actual activity will have to be carefully checked against the contracted levels of activity. Financial monitoring will be applied on a contract-by-contract basis. Invoices will be expected from all providers, with sample checks being applied to request further details of costs and procedures. Information about quality targets such as the length of waiting lists will also be required.

## Monitoring the overall position

Purchasers will need to be able to make sense of the mass of information the new system will generate. They will have a cash limit, which they must not exceed. Managers will have to make judgements about the amount of funds that must be kept in reserve to meet inflationary increases in contract costs, and to meet extracontractual referrals.

As districts gain experience in handling this information, they are likely to move towards cost-and-volume contracts. To monitor these, still more detailed information will be required. In many respects we are setting out to pay now for an information system which will serve us well into the next century. The development of an assessment of the health needs of the local population will certainly be evolutionary rather than revolutionary. However, the potential for large-scale research into health outcomes will grow as the system develops. Major health promotion initiatives with measurable target outcomes may not be very far away.

# The provider role

For the purposes of this section, the provider will be assumed to be a directly managed unit. However, the basic principles will easily adapt to the situation of an NHS trust. The information requirements of the provider fall into four main areas.

## Negotiating contracts

Managers in the unit will need information from their business plans in order to negotiate effectively over contracts. This may include quite detailed information about activity levels and the potential for increased activity with its effects on costs. Managers who have accurate information about how their service is currently running will be able to negotiate from a far stronger position than those who are uncertain about the true state of their units.

## Raising invoices

At first sight, raising invoices looks simple – all you have to do is send out a bill to the purchaser! However, in order to send out that bill, the provider will have to make sure that a system is in place which captures all the necessary data. For example, for each patient episode a unit will need to know the patient's place of residence and GP. Data capture in some departments with a high turnover such as out-patient departments will be very demanding.

Once the data have been captured, each patient episode will have to be matched to a contract, totalled, and an invoice sent at the agreed time.

*Data capture?*

## Supplying supporting data

All invoices will have to be supplied to the purchaser accompanied by a minimum data set of information to enable the purchaser to check the invoice against the contract. In cost-and-volume contracts, the calculation of the invoice will depend on the accuracy of this information. All providers will need to be able to supply information on quality measures specified in their contracts, and general managers are likely to seek this information well in advance of quality audits by purchasers.

### Monitoring the financial position of the unit

The unit will need to be able to reconcile income received against invoices sent out, and to chase up debts. The only source of a unit's income will be its contracts. The unit will need to develop accurate, timely, and relevant measures of clinical activity; it will also have to devise ways of costing that activity. This is more than a counting exercise, since managers will in future want answers to 'what if ...' questions, such as 'What if we take on a contract to do $x$ amount extra work in pathology? Will this affect our regular work? Will we need more staff or equipment, or can we work with what we have? If we need more resources, how much more? What is the minimum price we can set to make the contract financially viable?'

All units will need to have sophisticated financial information systems and finance specialists to support managers in interpreting the information generated and incorporating this into the business planning process for the future.

## Key Points for providers

A useful description of how provider units may organise their information systems was given by Palmer, Cruickshank, and Peel (1990), who divide the system into three areas:

- Front office activities – data capture and initial coding.
- Back office activities – invoicing and checking payments.
- Top office activities – monitoring overall performance.

## Memo Point 5.3

If you work in a provider unit, which 'office' do *you* work in?

## Summary Point

The development of information systems that can cope with funding by contracts will be the most difficult aspect of the White Paper changes to accomplish satisfactorily. It is not an issue which can be postponed. Whereas the internal market can develop over a period of time, adequate information systems to support contracts must be up and running immediately, because the only way a unit can secure the income for its services is by raising invoices, which will depend on relevant data capture, timely information processing, and accurate billing and monitoring procedures.

If you think carefully about Memo Point 5.3 you will see that every member of staff works for one of the 'offices'. We all supply and process information, and we all share the responsibility for its collection and ultimate use.

## Further Reading

One of the later Working Papers[1] is useful on the basic details. The Korner Reports [2-3] are still useful as a way of getting to grips with why we need to plan how we gather and use information. Palmer, Cruickshank, and Peel look at systems from the viewpoint of a provider[4] and a purchaser[5].

[1] Department of Health (1990), Working Paper No.11: *Framework for Information Systems: An Overview.* HMSO, London.
[2] Korner, E. (1982), *Steering Group on Health Services Information : first report to the Secretary of State.* HMSO, London.
[3] Windsor, P. (1986), Introducing Korner. *British Journal of Health Care Computing.* Weybridge, Surrey.
[4] Palmer, G., Cruickshank, J., Peel, V. (1990), Steps to milestone. *Health Service Journal,* **100,** pp.1568–1572.
[5] Cruickshank, J., Palmer, G., Peel, V., (1990), How to be an informed buyer. *Health Service Journal,* **100** (5223), pp.1573–1577.

# 6 — *Quality*

---

THIS SECTION IS DESIGNED TO HELP YOU TO :

● *Understand the Basis of a Quality Assurance System*

● *Decide How to Set Up Such a System in Your Work Area*

## Quality

Given that the avowed aim of *Working for Patients* is to bring all parts of the service up to the level of the best, improvements in the *quality* of the service available are essential. The competitive pressures introduced by the internal market include pressures to improve quality. Contracts will all contain detailed guarantees of *who* will deliver health services, *what* they will deliver, *when, where, why,* and *how* they will deliver them. This is what quality is all about.

However, it is not enough to write down quality guarantees – they must be delivered and be seen to be delivered. If you want people to meet quality standards, they must feel that they have had some involvement in setting those standards. This is where a quality assurance strategy comes in. It may be written for a whole unit, or it may be one that is applied to each department. An emphasis on 'getting it right first time' through total quality management means involvement in quality at all levels of the organisation.

It must be recognised that quality is not an absolute – there are different levels of quality, and quality costs money. The internal market at least allows purchasers to exercise some control over whatever compromises have to be made to balance quality and costs. Quality also needs 'assuring' – this means measuring what is happening against the agreed standards, and doing something about it if it is falling short.

People often feel very threatened by the 'assuring' element of quality management, seeing it as policing. It is possible to view it as a challenge: instead of 'Keep it quiet in case it's not up to standard', try to create a culture of 'Now we know how we're doing, let's work out how we can do it better'.

## Memo Point 6.1

What does the word 'quality' mean in terms of what *you* do in *your* work area? Spend a few moments thinking about this, then note down your ideas in the space below.

## Definition of quality

If you were to look up the word quality in a dictionary, you might find a definition of 'degree or grade of excellence', with 'excellence' defined as 'very good'. Other terms associated with the word quality are listed below.

- Quality (service) – one or more of the attributes or characteristics of a service which are important in terms of evaluating its worth.
- Quality control (a term borrowed from industry) – a system of identifying defects against previously agreed standards. A failed product can then be rejected before it reaches the customer.
- Quality improvement – enhancing the quality of a particular aspect of the service, such as improving the quality of access by reducing waiting lists or extending clinic opening hours.
- Quality assurance – preventing 'defects' in the first place, e.g. 'right first time', or 'consistently meeting the agreed expectations of the customer'.

Quality of care has long been a priority in the Health Service. This is a field where a single error can endanger life and/or cause immense amounts of distress. Errors can also be costly in financial terms; for example, financial liability for clinical errors will in future rest with district health authorities and NHS trusts.

## Memo Point 6.2

Think about a 'service' that you have used recently, such as a rail journey, a dry cleaning service, a car repair service, etc. What was good and what was bad about the quality of the service? Make notes on the detail that you can remember, then form an overall judgement of the service you received. How will your experience of good or bad quality affect your future use of this service?

## Quality expectations

Some of your comments in Memo Point 6.2 might relate to the cost of the service and whether it represented good or bad value for money in terms of waiting time, how you were treated, whether the service helped you to achieve what you wanted, etc.

Most people judge services or products against previous experience, or come to expect certain things because of publicity or feedback from others. Whether or not they use the service again will depend not only upon quality, but upon whether there are any alternatives available. In Health Service terms, one consequence of the internal market may be that there will be a greater choice of providers in the medium to longer term. Already purchasers, particularly GP fund holders in close touch with patients, are making clear and consistent demands through negotiations over service specifications. These demands need to be realistic. There is no new money in the system as a result of the changes, and we have seen that there have to be compromises between cost and quality. Nevertheless, consistent pressure from purchasers will be passed on throughout the system and will affect staff at all levels in provider units. For the benefit of patients it is important that each department responds to reasonable demands and sees them as challenges rather than threats.

## Memo Point 6.3

Imagine yourself as the patient of a provider unit. List the five quality criteria by which you would judge the service you receive.

When you have done this, compare your ideas with those in the quality sections of the general and service specifications shown in the Appendix. Ask yourself if the purchasers and providers are sensitive to the patient's viewpoint. Should service specifications be available to the general public so that they can assess quality for themselves?

# Developing a quality assurance strategy for your work area

Most specifications will require units or departments to have a written quality assurance strategy. The remainder of this chapter aims to help you to begin writing one for your area.

## Making a start

Units or departments wanting to set up a quality assurance system have three choices:

- They can 'take from the shelf' someone else's work on the subject.
- They can appoint an 'expert' to produce one.
- They can use the expertise and knowledge of their own staff to produce one.

'Off-the-shelf' packages have a place in a comprehensive quality assurance strategy; however, they are almost all ways of policing what is happening, and sometimes the standards they police are not the ones you require. They can be helpful in identifying quality problems systematically, but they will do little or nothing to help you find a solution to them.

'Experts' are hard to find. They tend to write elegant documents which tell you what you already know, and once again leave you to do the real work of implementing the strategy yourself. There is a value in having someone who drives quality issues throughout the organisation, provided that this person does not also seek to drive through his own personal solutions to quality problems. There must be room for collaborative involvement of staff at every level.

You and your staff are the essential ingredients in a quality assurance strategy. You are the ones who really know your work and who actually provide the service. Teamwork is the key: at some stage it is essential that the expertise and knowledge of everyone is used. They must be involved in creating, implementing and monitoring the strategy if it is to be anything more than a paper document.

## *Four steps towards a strategy*

1. Map out the component parts of your work area.
2. Identify your consumers.
3. Determine your standards.
4. Decide on methods of evaluation.

### Map out the component parts of your work area

This map needs to be more comprehensive than you may at first think. For example, the component parts of a residential service to people with a mental handicap comprise the following:

● Physical environment.
● Social environment.
● Staffing (including support staff).
● Choices/opportunities for clients.
● Assessment of individual needs of clients.
● Occupation of clients.
● Attention to physical wellbeing.
● Staff training and development.
● Administrative procedures.
● Teamwork/communication.

Each of the above can then be broken down further into microcomponents. For example, the physical environment breaks down into the following:

● Number of bathrooms/toilets available.
● Cleanliness of the house.
● Heating.
● Health and safety.
● Anything not covered by the above.

## Memo Point 6.4

Map out the component parts of your work area. Decide for yourself how much detail you need to include, and which divisions are the most useful to you.

## Identify your consumers

This is another task that is more complex than it first appears. 'Consumers' are the people who actually use your services. If you are working in a hospital clinical area, patients or residents are the ones who will come to mind first, but should you also consider visitors, and family or friends who have telephone contact with you? Where do GPs or community nurses fit into your definition?

If you are working in a non-clinical area, you will still have to identify your consumers. For example, a personnel department might define its consumers as all the staff of the unit. A pathology laboratory might see its consumers as the consultants and GPs who have ordered the investigations. However, it might also help to see the patients as the ultimate consumers of its service.

## Memo Point 6.5

Identify the consumers of your service and list them in the space below:

## Determine your standards

For each of the components of your service, you should set the standards your consumers expect, and that you can realistically deliver. In the section on business planning we looked at objectives, and decided that they should be relevant, achievable, and measurable. The same applies to quality standards. Some will derive from government initiatives such as the *Patients' Charter;* others will be embodied in contracts, and yet others will be standards that you and your staff choose for yourselves.

### An example of a set of standards for out-patient services

1. No patient should have to wait for an urgent out-patient appointment.

2. No patient should wait for more than 6 weeks for an initial non-urgent out-patient appointment.

3. A booked admission system should operate for all patients with 90% of out-patients needing admission being given a firm appointment date.

4. Waiting time in out-patient clinics should not exceed 30 minutes from appointment time, before the patient is seen by a member of the medical staff. If delays are unavoidable, patients should be told the reasons for the delay and how long it will last.

5. All new referrals should be reviewed by a consultant. They should normally be seen by a consultant, associate specialist, or senior registrar at the first (new) attendance at an out-patient clinic.

## Memo Point 6.6

Now to try to draft some quality standards for the component parts of your area, bearing in mind consumer expectations. This is best done as a team task, but for the purposes of this exercise produce some draft standards on your own. The reason is to ensure that you are confident in your knowledge of how to draw up standards, so that you can be confident in helping other members of your team.

When you have drafted some standards, check to see that they are *relevant, achievable,* and *measurable.*

## Decide on methods of evaluation

We have said that quality standards must be measurable, or in other words, it must be possible to evaluate them. A wide variety of evaluation methods is available, but most require time and effort to organise if the resulting information is to have any value. Frequently used methods of evaluation are as follows:

- Customer satisfaction surveys.
- Sampling procedures using open questions.
- Informal interviews with staff and clients.
- Formal interviews.
- Non-participant observation.
- Experience of a service 'through the eyes' of a consumer.

In some cases information systems will have to be set up to capture the data needed for evaluation on a continuous basis. In other cases, such as consumer satisfaction surveys, an attempt will be made to sample consumer opinion at a specified point in time. For example, let us take the first of the standards described earlier for an out-patient department: 'No patient should wait more than 6 weeks for an initial non-urgent out-patient appointment.'

If the appointments system is computerised, it may be possible to automatically compare the date of appointment with the date of referral, and regularly identify any delays or other problems. If the system is not computerised, a manual recording system will be needed. Someone will have to sit down and do the necessary calculations at regular intervals.

## Memo Point 6.7

Now take the standards you drafted at Memo Point 6.6 and state how you propose to evaluate each of them.

# Summary Point

*The way forward*

As with the business plan, a department's quality assurance strategy will need to be compatible with the overall unit approach to quality. You should do this by incorporating a final 'portfolio' check into your quality plan:

● Are you and other managers committed to it?
● Are consumer expectations included?
● Are you covering too much?
● Are you covering too little?
● Who should evaluate?
● How often should you evaluate?
● How will you provide feedback to service providers?
● What type of feedback will you provide?
● How will recommendations for change be acted upon?

Developing a quality assurance strategy may at first appear an awesome task, but it is well worth the effort. Some people think of quality assurance as an exercise for cost-cutting, annual inspection, managers not trusting staff, and so on. If you involve your team in building a realistic strategy, you will see that quality assurance is good for staff as well as for consumers. It can help a team to identify problem areas and to act upon them, with benefit to consumers and staff alike.

# Further Reading

An emphasis on quality is not unique to *Working for Patients*. However, contracts have emphasised the importance of being able to measure it.[1] This has given an impetus to audit in all the healthcare professions.[2-4]

[1] Department of Health (1989), Working Paper No. 6: *Medical Audit*. HMSO, London.
[2] Pollock, A. and Evans, M. (1989), *Surgical Audit*. Butterworths, London.
[3] Pearson, A. (ed.) (1989), *Nursing Quality Measurement*. John Wiley and Sons Ltd., Chichester.
[4] Goldstone, L.A., Ball, J.A. and Collier, M.M. (1983) *Monitor*. Newcastle upon Tyne Polytechnic Products Ltd., Ellison Place, Newcastle upon Tyne NE1 8ST.

# 7 — Marketing

THIS SECTION IS DESIGNED TO HELP YOU TO :

● *Understand What Marketing Means*

● *Explore How the Idea of Marketing Can Be Applied to the NHS*

● *Draft a Marketing Plan For Your Own Area*

*Most people mistakenly think of marketing as no more than advertising or sales promotion.*

# Marketing and the NHS

Kotler (1975) defines marketing as 'The satisfaction of consumer needs through coordinated effort in order to achieve organisational goals.' Most people think of marketing in terms of what they see on television and in the newspapers, in terms of advertising and promotion alone. Such a limited definition would be of little value in the context of the NHS.

## Memo Point 7.1

Think for a moment about Kotler's definition of marketing. How can you apply it to your own area? Who are your consumers and what do they need? What are these organisational goals that you are trying to achieve? Note down your own ideas.

**Marketing in the NHS means ... being responsive to the people who use our services**

This is one of the fundamental ideas behind *Working for Patients*. A major criticism of the NHS has always been that it is a very large organisation that decides for itself what is best for patients, and then develops its services accordingly. Patients are expected to be grateful for what they are offered, and put up with delays or other inadequacies because we tell them we are short of resources.

The idea of marketing can be used to turn this on its head. It may be useful occasionally to think of patients as 'customers', even though they do not purchase our services directly. If we were running a business and customer dissatisfaction were increasing, as it seems to be in the NHS, we would place a high priority on finding out what our customers wanted, and making sure that we delivered the goods.

We need to be clear what we mean by the term 'customer' and also the related term 'consumer'. A customer is someone who buys goods or services; a consumer is someone who uses or 'consumes' those goods or services. In the world of commerce, customers and consumers are frequently the same; the internal market of the Health Service is inevitably more complicated! In Health Service terms, customers are purchasers. The main ones are the district health authorities and GP fund holders, who are responsible for 'buying' health services on behalf of the local population. The consumers are the people who *use* health services – patients, clients and residents.

However, just because our patients do not pay directly for health services does not mean that we cannot apply the idea of marketing in the sense of being responsive to all our contacts with them. When a member of staff does something for a patient, the way that staff member responds to the patient's needs will influence how the patient views the service we provide. The patient may write a letter of congratulation or complaint, which will be noted in a report on service quality sent to purchasers. The patient may go to his GP and tell him about the service he has received. Consumers have real influence over purchasers, if they choose to use it. If they complain to purchasers, the purchasers have a responsibility to ensure that providers act on those complaints, and so the service will change.

At a different level, we can see marketing as being responsive to the health needs of our local population. For example, if we live in an area with a higher than average number of elderly people in the population, what do those elderly people require of a Health Service, and to what extent have we committed resources to meet their needs?

Because of the *Working for Patients* changes, marketing can become very useful to us if we interpret the term sensibly, and use it to concentrate our thoughts on how to become more responsive to the needs of those who purchase and use our services.

## Developing a marketing plan

One way of ensuring that a unit is responsive to the needs of purchasers is to develop a marketing plan. Individual departments or clinical areas can also develop marketing plans, which will then form part of the plan for the unit as a whole. There are four steps in the development of a marketing plan:

- Decide who are your customers and your consumers.
- Decide what you propose and what you are able to provide for them.
- Provide as much of it as you can.
- Tell your customers and consumers what you are doing.

Viewed in this light, there have always been marketing initiatives in the NHS, but often they have been isolated one-off projects, rather than truly integrated into the whole of the service we provide.

There may be a temptation for those working in directly managed units to say that finding out the health needs of the local population is the responsibility of the district health authority. It is certainly true that one potential benefit of the purchaser/provider split is to allow district health authorities to set contracts with providers in such a way that they have to respond to the local health needs. However, providers would be very naive if they did not try to anticipate those local health needs through their own research, and to build those needs into their business plans at the earliest possible stage. Again, providers will want to ensure that purchasers (the customers) know about the changes they have made and can see how they are responding to their demands. This is a form of promotion.

It is also possible to use the marketing theme to examine how different departments within one unit respond to each other. A surgeon may be seen as a purchaser of the services of diagnostic departments or nursing care in surgical wards, but the analogy must not be pushed too far, or damaging divisions may develop within a unit. However, the idea of encouraging departments to explore the needs of those who draw on their services as part of planning care for patients is worth exploring.

*Marketing in the sense of being responsive to our customers and consumers is the responsibility of all staff at all levels of the service.*

## Step-by-step planning

### Step 1: Who are your clients?

The word client is here defined to include both customers and consumers. Some areas may concentrate their marketing effort on the customers, the purchasing organisations, while others may find it valuable to use marketing ideas to promote closer relationships with consumers. The clients you identify will depend on where in the organisation you are working. A senior manager of a provider unit might choose to consider the unit as a whole – thinking in terms of which purchasing agencies the unit might contract to serve. Middle or junior managers might choose to think about their own departments or clinical areas. The following is a list of some potential clients:

- Patients/residents.
- Families.
- GPs.
- Health authorities.
- Local authorities.
- The employees in your unit.
- Potential employees.
- Other departments in your unit.

# Memo Point 7.2

Name your clients and write brief notes to explain the reasons for your choices. Can you usefully divide them into customers and consumers?

## *Step 2: What do your clients want?*

Begin by reviewing the present position – what goods or services do you currently provide for your clients? If you are a manager, you will need to answer this question in considerable detail. Modern technology can help with the collection of data, but it is up to you to analyse what you have collected and to make sense of it. Are there any aspects of the services you currently provide where you feel that you lack information?

What will your clients want in terms of quantity or quality of service in the future? How much do you really know about this? There may be national surveys or extensive regional research that can tell you something about major trends. Have there been any local surveys to identify client satisfactions and dissatisfactions? Do you know your clients personally – for example, local GPs or social services managers? It will be very easy to say 'It's their responsibility, not mine, to make the first move', but if you choose to take on board the marketing concept, you can no longer give this answer. The provider must make the first move, always.

# Memo Point 7.3

Name one aspect of your existing service about which you lack accurate information. What are you going to do about it?

Jot down some notes on what you think your clients want in terms of service quality and quantity.

How can you find out more about the needs of your clients?

## Step 3: Now you know what your clients want, what are you going to do about it?

Some of what your clients want will be impossible for you to achieve, at least in the short term. Do you have a responsibility to explain this to them? Some things will take time and energy, but are realistically achievable. Some things can be put right immediately. It is very important that you demonstrate in a tangible way that you are capable of responding to client need.

Many managers see marketing in terms of *product, price, place,* and *promotion:* these are the four key items you can potentially control, therefore you need to find ways of varying them to achieve the right 'marketing mix' for your customers and consumers. *Product* can be translated into *service,* since most Health Service work involves doing things for patients, rather than giving them something they can take away. *Price* is likely to be a senior management responsibility. However, the staffing mix and the use of products in a department will directly affect the price the unit has to charge to make itself financially viable. *Place* is something hospital staff tend to take for granted – if a patient wants treatment he comes to the hospital. But one consequence of giving providers freedom to manage their units in their own way is that it allows staff to innovate. Would a mobile day service be welcome in the local area? Is there any scope for moving out-patient clinics to sites closer to where patients live? *Promotion* means advertising material, but it also means personal contact. It is more than selling. Every time a patient comes in contact with your service is an opportunity for promotion, in the sense of trying to ensure that you respond to his needs. Even if you are not in direct contact with consumers, you may have contact with customers. The same principles apply.

## Memo Point 7.4

You can use the marketing concept to give direction to your department or clinical area. Jot down notes on goals or changes to the marketing mix that you could make in your area, and that you think would improve the service.

*Step 4: Tell your clients what you are doing for them*

Don't be shy! If your team has had some good ideas and put time and effort into implementing them, tell everyone about them

First, tell your 'customers', so that they know you are responding to their needs. Second, tell your managers so that they know what a good job you are doing, and so that they can take account of your initiatives as part of the overall monitoring of the service. Make sure you gather detailed information on the effect of your initiatives. In many cases this evidence will be needed to demonstrate that your unit is active in fulfilling the quality conditions of its contracts. Third, tell other departments and clinical areas, to encourage them to apply and develop your ideas for themselves.

## Memo Point 7.5

Take one of the changes you propose to introduce. Who will you tell about it? How will you advertise and promote it?

## Summary Point

If you have worked through this chapter with care and given time to the Memo Points, you will already have produced the first draft of your marketing plan. It will need refining and discussing with others, but the basic ideas are probably in your mind right now. It is up to you to take them, put them into practice, and learn from the process.

- There is more to marketing than advertising or selling.
- Identify your 'customers' and 'consumers'.
- Find out what they want.
- Give them as much as you can.
- Tell them what you are doing.
- Use these ideas to make the NHS more responsive to patients.

## Further Reading

Many of the general texts on marketing need a lot of hard work to adapt the ideas to the Byzantine subtleties of the internal market in the NHS. Kotler[1] is expensive, but a good starting point. The articles look at the topic from an overall NHS perspective,[2] and from a view of what GPs are looking for.[3]

[1] Kotler, P. and Andreasen, A. R. (1975), *Strategic Marketing for Non-profit Organisations*. Prentice Hall, Englewood Cliffs, New Jersey.
[2] Keleher, R. and Cole, C. (1989), Marketing. Is it really relevant to the NHS? *Health Services Management*, **85** (1), pp.30–33
[3] Sargent, J. (1991), Knowing your market. *Health Service Journal*, **101** (5238), pp.24–25.

# 8 — *Managing Change*

---

THIS SECTION IS DESIGNED TO HELP YOU TO :

● *Review the Main Changes Arising From 'Working For Patients'*

● *Understand the Basic Principles of Change Management*

● *Make a Plan to Manage the Changes in Your Own Work Area*

## Managing change

It is important that everyone in the Health Service understands the main changes that *Working for Patients* introduces. In this book we have left aside political views about the rights and wrongs of the system, and instead concentrated on how to introduce and manage the changes at local level for the benefit of patients.

Although the new system is finance-led, it is likely to affect the working practices of everyone in the Health Service. Anyone who has responsibility for managing any part of the system will have to change some of the ways things are done in their area. However, the way that change is introduced at this local level will make a significant difference to the outcome in terms of ultimate patient benefit. This chapter is designed to help you to think through how you will introduce any changes in your own work area. The section will cover understanding the main changes; identifying the benefits; and planning the process of change. The chapter begins with a number of Memo Points, because introducing change is an active process. The only right answers are the ones you find for yourself.

# Introducing the White Paper changes

It is important that everyone who works in the NHS understands the main changes that arise from the implementation of *Working for Patients*. We also need to think through how and why those changes may affect us in our own working area. To begin with, review the main changes:

- Money will follow the patient.
- Purchasers and providers will agree contracts.
- Providers will have more responsibility for managing their own units.
- Some GPs will become fund holders.
- Some units will become NHS trusts.
- All units will develop business planning.
- New information systems will be needed.
- Quality standards will be specified in contracts.

## Memo Point 8.1

Review the main changes of *Working for Patients* and list the ones that will most affect you in your work area. How do you feel about the changes as a whole? Has working through this book changed the way you view any of them?

## Memo Point 8.2

Many of the changes will have advantages and disadvantages for both staff and patients. In practice, the benefit and loss balance sheet will probably depend on *how* we implement the changes. The first stage in this process is to gain a commitment from as many of your staff and colleagues as you can to making the changes work.

Take one of the proposals that you think has a lot to offer, and imagine you have to give a talk about it to your staff or colleagues. What benefits would you pick out for them as staff, and also as potential patients?

## Memo Point 8.3

Think now about the disadvantages of the changes. List the ones that most trouble you. Will your worries be different from those of your staff and colleagues, or the same?

## The process of managing change

People working at all levels of the organisation must give attention to the process of introducing and managing the *Working for Patients* changes, so that the inevitable stress is kept to a minimum. Basic principles will be to ensure that information is widely available, that staff are supported by their managers when implementing change, and that managers take into account the views of their staff when deciding how best to introduce new ways of working.

For these purposes you should understand the basic principles of change management and design strategies to minimise stress.

### Some change strategies

There are many textbooks on this subject, and many models of managing change. We will examine a number of well tried and tested strategies, and see how they relate to our tasks. This section will help you to explore six different strategies you can embody into a managing change plan for your area:

- Strategy one:     Create ownership and involvement.
- Strategy two:     Create a positive environment for change.
- Strategy three:   Identify the need for change with staff.
- Strategy four:    Work with staff to devise an *action plan*.
- Strategy five:    Communicate the changes.
- Strategy six:     Anticipate conflicts and resistance.

## Strategy one: Create ownership and involvement

This is paramount for successful change management. Much of the preceding work in this chapter has centred around gaining a thorough understanding of the changes. This is a strategy which can be used for all staff. In planning your strategy you will need to examine ways of doing the following:

- Ensuring that all your staff *understand* the changes.
- Trying to make the changes *relevant* to them. Often their first thoughts are 'how will this affect me?'
- Making sure your staff can see the benefits of the changes to their work. This usually involves ultimate benefits to patients.
- Finally, you need to get your staff *involved* in the changes.

This chapter cannot tell you how to do all these things, it can only highlight the issues. You may, of course, like to discuss these issues with your colleagues.

## Strategy two: Create a positive environment for change

The values of a positive environment as one of the recipes for managing change are well documented in management and allied literature. Creating such an environment involves:

- Being positive about the changes you propose to introduce.
- Listening and responding to concerns.
- Sensitively supporting people involved in changes.
- Being open about problems and solutions.
- Encouraging questioning and supporting initiative.
- Reducing as much as you can the negative forces of change, such as limited resources, time, constraints, and negative attitudes.
- Emphasising that we all have some power and some responsibility in deciding how the changes will work in practice.

## Strategy three: Identify the need for change

Start from the assumption that the system we used to have was not perfect. Potentially the changes give us a chance to improve things. Any change can unfreeze old working practices and make innovation possible. For example, compare the new funding arrangements with the old ones.

The national formula for financing the National Health Service is now considered to be out of date, and did not always take into account all the factors relevant to healthcare. At unit level, increased resources did not follow increased activity.

## Memo Point 8.4

For each of the main themes of *Working for Patients*, write down in one or two sentences what it was about that aspect of the service that the White Paper was designed to improve.

## Strategy four: Work with staff to develop an action plan for change

Once the changes that are needed have been identified, the 'action plan' approach can be used. It may be possible to involve staff in devising the action plan; they should certainly be involved in the implementation of that plan.

Specify the target dates for the completion of action plan items and stick to them. Steady progress encourages motivation and raises staff spirits and commitment to change.

The preconditions of success for all in working out such an action plan might include:

● Allocated time away from operational duties.
● Senior management leading by example.
● Communication, communication, communication.

Action plans often have resource implications and these need to be identified. Resources may be needed for:

- Training.
- Recruitment.
- Communication.
- Quality.

## Memo Point 8.5

Make a list of changes necessary in your work area as a result of the White Paper.

### Strategy five: Communicate the changes

It is important that you communicate your ideas for change in a way your staff can understand. One way of doing this is by holding formal and informal meetings to 'sell' your ideas of change. You should be ready for challenges or lack of understanding. You should persevere professionally with your ideas and stick to your reasons why changes are necessary.

In such meetings your interpersonal skills will need to be sharpened. For example, you should concentrate on the following:

- Ability to transmit facts, ideas, and feelings to others.
- Listening skills.
- Being an advocate; having the ability to reason and justify ideas or courses of action.
- Leading and motivating others.
- Ability to evaluate and criticise the contributions of others in a manner that encourages rather than threatens them.
- Ability to accept criticism from others without being over-defensive.

Consider the following ideas for communicating clearly what you are doing:

- Newsletters.
- Lunchtime seminars.
- Team briefings.
- Appraisals.
- Meetings.
- Distance learning.

Personal contacts will open up your access to other people, and openly support and disseminate your ideas for change. Getting around and talking to people will enhance your credibility and reputation. It will also influence and support your programme for change.

### Strategy six: Anticipate conflicts and resistance
Get to know why people might resist the proposed changes.

# Memo Point 8.6

Make a list of why people generally resist change; try to relate your points directly to aspects of *Working for Patients*. For example, one reason may be uncertainty about the future – they may feel that the role of their particular department is changing, and that they are not sure whether they have a role in the new scheme of things.

So, how can you help individuals to overcome their resistance and adapt as quickly as possible to change? Openness and flexibility on your part will encourage questioning and the expression of difficulties.

## Summary Point

One of the first steps in overcoming any barriers to change is to determine who in the organisation will see the changes as beneficial. It will be vital to harness the enthusiasm of these individuals and to use them to provide direction and impetus in the change management programme. The reasons for their view of the change may be varied:

● Clinical staff seeing the changes as an opportunity to develop their department.
● Those dissatisfied with current service levels.
● Those who can see the potential of a better service.

If you have worked through this chapter with care and given time to the exercises, you should have a better understanding of the proposed changes and how they will affect you, your staff, and your department, and the NHS as a whole. In addition, you should be in a much better position to introduce any changes into your own area with the minimum of disruption.

## Further Reading

There are many good general management textbooks about managing change,[1] but most need adapting to the specialist constraints of the NHS. Two publications that deal with this topic specifically from an NHS viewpoint are worth citing: the Open University book[2] is available only as part of a complete management training package; however, many Health Service libraries will have bought copies for reference purposes. The primary care book[3] is clear and realistic. Its examples are mainly from the perspective of a GP practice, but the principles illustrated are easily transferable to community and secondary care.

[1] Leigh, A. (1988), *Effective Change*. Institute of Personnel Management, London.
[2] Open University (1990), *Managing Health Services B782: Book 9: Managing Change*. Open University, Milton Keynes.
[3] Pringle, M. *et al.* (1991), *Managing Change in Primary Care*. Radcliffe Medical Press, Oxford.

# Appendix A

---

## Glossary of Terms and Abbreviations

**Block Contract**
A contract in which services are bought as a block, for one overall sum of money, instead of pricing according to the number of people who use the services.

**Capital Charges**
An accounting device which makes providers pay interest on their capital assets, meaning buildings, equipment, and land.

**Capital Funding** – *see* **Resident Funding**

**Caring For People**
The 1989 White Paper that accompanied *Working for Patients* and dealt with social services and community health arrangements. It was incorporated into the *NHS and Community Care Act* 1990, but its implementation was delayed.

**Consumer**
In marketing terms, one who uses the goods or services sold. The person may or may not be the same as the buyer.

**Contract**
In NHS terms this is a non-legally binding agreement between a purchaser and a provider, stating the quantity, quality and cost of the health services described in the agreement.

**Cost-and-volume Contract**
A contract where the price varies according to the volume of patients who use the service. It usually contains a **block** payment for treating up to a specified number of patients, and then a **cost-per-case** element for any additional patients treated.

**Cost Improvement**
A requirement that NHS units lower their costs by improving their efficiency. Targets are usually set at an annual percentage of the total cost of the service.

**Cost-per-case Contract**
A contract in which the cost of each patient treatment is agreed and paid for individually.

**Customer**
In marketing terms this is the purchaser, the person who actually buys the goods or services.

**Directly Managed Unit (DMU)**
A provider unit in which the unit general manager is directly accountable to the district general manager. The health authority retains overall power to control the service development plans of the unit.

**District Health Authority (DHA)**
The body that purchases health care on behalf of all local residents, except for a limited list of procedures for those people registered with **GP fund holders.** It also manages **directly managed units.**

**District Information Support Systems (DISS)**
Computerised systems for handling the audit and other data the **district health authority** needs in order to perform its role. Systems may be shared with provider units to reduce duplication of input.

**Extracontractual Referral (ECR)**
When a GP refers a patient to a provider unit with which the DHA does not have a contract. Each DHA needs to hold back a portion of its budget to cover these on a cost-per-case basis.

**Family Health Services Authorities (FHSAs)**
The bodies that administer the contracts for primary health services, including GP practices, dentists, etc. Formerly known as family practitioner committees.

**GP Fund Holders**
Larger general practices that hold public funds and use them to purchase defined health services on behalf of the patients on their lists.

**Human Resource Management**
In the NHS this term encompasses personnel functions, with the addition of pay structuring and bargaining, and workforce review and planning. Particularly relevant in **NHS trusts,** where employment contracts are locally set.

**Indicative Drug Budgets**
A scheme by which GP prescribing is monitored against national averages. This is used to set notional budgets which 'indicate' the level of spending per patient suggested by national averages. GPs have to

explain and justify significant overspending.

## Korner
A set of reports on information in the NHS compiled by a steering group led by Baroness Korner. The detailed work of the group has been superseded by the new finance system, but the principle of collecting data in a systematic and nationally agreed way remains an important target.

## Manpower and Personnel System
Part of a unit or district information system, comprising computerised records of all members of the workforce.

## Marketing Mix
The four factors that can be varied when selling the *product* or service itself, its *price*, the *place* where it is offered, and the way it is *promoted*.

## Medical Audit
The system whereby doctors mutually compare their patterns of clinical activity in order to identify the best practice. Frequently the outcome is a 'protocol', or set of guidelines on good practice. Each district and FHA must set up a Medical Audit Advisory Group to organise and support medical audit.

## Minimum Data Set
A term developed by **Korner.** It is the minimum data that must be collected to generate the information required. In NHS contract terms, it means the minimum amount of data needed for a purchaser to be able to monitor a provider's contract performance.

## NHS and Community Care Act 1990
The Act of Parliament which turned the provisions of *Working For Patients* and *Caring For People* into law.

## NHS Trust
A unit run by a board of trustees and not accountable to the district health authority. It has greater freedom than a directly managed unit to run its own services, including setting local terms of employment for all staff, and managing its capital assets. Sometimes termed 'self-governing' units.

## Patient Administration System (PAS)
A mainly computerised record system that receives data about admissions, treatment and other clinical activity for each patient. Under the new finance system, purchasers need some of this information to monitor contracts, while providers need a detailed picture of clinical activity to track their costs and predict future activity patterns.

## Portfolio Planning

A business planning term. 'Portfolio' is a term taken from the stockmarket, but here refers to the range of plans produced by the different departments of a provider unit. Thus 'portfolio planning' means reviewing how the plans of one department affect those of another, *before* making decisions about which parts of the business plan should go ahead.

## Provider

In NHS terms this a unit that offers health services, i.e. that treats patients, residents, or clients. Notice that the term can be applied to private hospitals as well as to NHS units.

## Purchaser

In NHS terms, this is a body that holds public funds and uses them to buy health services on behalf of the people it serves.

## Resident Funding

Distribution of public money for the NHS according to the number of people who live in each district

## Resource Management

An imprecise term that generally refers to the establishment of computerised databases that will generate information to enable service managers and clinicians to manage their resources efficiently and effectively. Thus **patient administration systems, manpower and personnel systems,** and financial management systems are all encompassed in the term 'resource management'.

## Rolling Contract

A contract for a specified period (for example 3 years), which is renegotiated annually. Thus it rolls forward for the next 3 years if the negotiation is successful, and the provider always has a long period of notice should the contract not be renewed.

## Service Agreement

Another name for an NHS contract.

## Service Specification

The details of the services the purchaser requires of the provider.

## SWOT Analysis

A business planning term. SWOT is Strengths, Weaknesses, Opportunities and Threats. It is a way of focusing one's thoughts on the current market environment and on how one is performing in that environment.

**Tertiary Referrals**
Referral by a hospital consultant of an in-patient from his own hospital to another hospital. This has the same financial implications as an **extracontractual referral** if the second hospital does not have a contract with the district of origin.

**Working For Patients**
The 1989 White Paper that announced the new system. It was supplemented by a series of detailed working papers, and largely incorporated into law in the **NHS and Community Care Act** 1990.

# *Appendix B*

---

**Sample Contract Documents**

# DOCUMENT 1

**General Conditions Relating to the Provision of
Healthcare Services**

**Blankshire Health Authority**

**and**

**Blankby Hospital**

**(Directly Managed Unit)**

## 1 Purpose of the Agreement

The purpose of the agreement is to specify agreed standards and quantitative performance measures of service, cost-efficiency and effectiveness, recognising that the authority and the unit are dedicated to working together to provide high-quality, cost-effective health care responsive to the needs of the local community.

The agreement is not legally binding but provides a framework for the provision of specified services by the unit in return for an agreed level of funding. It is anticipated that both parties will abide by the conditions of the agreement, apart from any exceptional circumstances following which both would be expected to negotiate a further agreement.

The authority's short-term programme process will provide the opportunity to influence variations to the agreement through formal negotiation and the authority's established planning and review processes.

## 2 Agreement Period

The agreement will commence on 1 April 19●● and continue as a rolling 3-year contract, thus providing stability to the provider. The agreement will be formally reviewed on an annual basis with any variations agreed between both parties, and reasonable notice of changes agreed jointly. Such periods of notice will be discussed and agreed by both parties.

## 3 Performance of Service

During the period of the agreement the unit will perform the services as detailed in the attached schedule, and in accordance with the conditions contained in this agreement.

## 4 Scope of the Agreement

The agreement includes all goods, materials, equipment, labour, transport and everything else that is necessary in order for the unit to supply the services required.

## 5 Location of Service Provision

The unit will provide the services specified in the attached schedule, within the sites detailed in the schedule, unless otherwise agreed in writing by the authority.

## 6 Variation of Service

The authority reserves the right, in exceptional circumstances, to modify the specification by giving reasonable notice in writing. Equally, in the eventuality of any quantitative data in the specification changing – for example, changes in case-mix – the authority would wish to negotiate a variation. Similarly the unit may wish to initiate discussions on variations. Where applicable, any alteration to the service fee arising out of such modifications will be the subject of separate negotiation between the authority and the unit.

In the most exceptional circumstances, including major disaster or other untoward incidents, the authority or the unit may have to set aside this agreement either wholly or in part. In these circumstances there will be full discussions between the authority and the unit general manager.

## 7 Service Fee

The fee for the service is as stated in the attached schedule (not included in this sample).

The unit will cooperate fully with the authority to supply financial information in order to demonstrate the costing structure of the contract and to enable the authority to meet its statutory obligations in regard to financial controls, including statements relating to income and expenditure.

## 8 Variation of Service Fee

The service fee will remain firm for the first year of the agreement, unless negotiated and agreed otherwise by the unit and the authority. Failing agreement, the matter will be decided by arbitration in accordance with the provisions of paragraph 14.

Service developments will be planned and agreed through the authority's formal planning process, which will follow the short-term programme guidelines as amended from time to time.

## 9 Inflation

Units will be expected to contain inflation within an overall figure of 6%. Of this, 5% will be additional funding and 1% will be cash-releasing cost-improvement monies. Should inflation exceed 6%, the authority will negotiate with the unit and agree the most appropriate means of dealing with any shortfall.

## 10 Cost Improvements

The unit will be expected to make a 1% cash-releasing cost-improvement during 19●●.

## 11 Payment Arrangements

Payments will be made during the second half of each month by instalments.

## 12 Performance Monitoring and Quality of Service

The unit will:

a) Be responsible for ensuring that services are provided to the standards and levels detailed in the specification.
b) Provide the authority with details of its quality control and monitoring procedures, which must be regularly reviewed.
c) Comply with the agreed admission and discharge procedures.

d) Provide evidence of the establishment and maintenance of effective control of infection procedures.

e) Be required to cooperate with other units and district officers in the management and notification of infectious diseases.

f) Be required to cooperate with other units and district officers in the event of a major disaster.

g) Provide the authority with information in accordance with national, regional and district procedures. This must include Korner minimum data on activity, finance and manpower, together with standard Department of Health waiting lists and waiting times.

h) Participate fully in the corporate development of the authority's information technology strategy and in the operation of the authority's computerised information systems, ensuring that data are input and maintained in an accurate and timely manner.

i) Provide evidence of working towards the principles of the authority's Patients' Charter, and wherever possible adhering to it.

j) Follow the authority's agreed complaints procedure, providing evidence that complaints are dealt with quickly and effectively, and that they are used to identify areas for improvement.

k) Produce a quality assurance strategy, together with evidence of effective monitoring procedures.

l) Meet the requirements of national training bodies such as the Royal Colleges and ENB in quality and service delivery. This should include the provision of postgraduate facilities and access to library services. Copies of reports received from such bodies must be provided immediately to the district general manager.

m) Support the review cycle as outlined in the district's medical audit programme.

n) Encourage research into clinical practice or service delivery. Such research should be supported by an ethical committee constituted in accordance with HSC(IS)153.

o) Participate in the development of nursing audit and information systems.

p) Provide evidence of working towards meeting the requirements of the authority's *Standards for Nursing Services* and the Department of Health's *Strategy for Nursing* document.

q) Provide evidence of a continuing programme to ensure that communal and reception patient areas are welcoming and of a high quality of decoration and comfort.

r) Undertake customer satisfaction surveys.

s) Produce evidence to demonstrate that waiting lists are managed equitably.

t) Advise the purchase of plans to achieve junior doctor rotas of 1/3 or 1/4 in the short and medium term.

u) Provide health promotion programmes appropriate to the specialty and patients' personal needs.

v) Provide counselling services appropriate to patients' personal needs.

## 13 Unsatisfactory Performance

In the event of the unit failing substantially to provide the agreed level or quality of service, the authority will discuss methods of improving and reinstating the service levels. The authority reserves the right to appropriately adjust the level of funding of the contract following discussion with the unit.

## 14 Arbitration

It is recognised that it is in the interests of both parties to resolve any disagreements locally by joint discussion between the authority and the unit.

In the event of an unresolved dispute arising out of the agreement, the matter will be dealt with in the first instance by the regional general manager. If this does not resolve the dispute to the satisfaction of both parties, the matter can be referred to the Secretary of State or his appointee, whose decisions will be binding.

## 15 Inspections

The unit will at all times allow access to the authority and its officers to inspect the records and documents of the unit that directly relate to the services provided, and to take extracts or copies as necessary.

Throughout this agreement the unit will allow the authority's members and officers, together with the Community Health Council and other persons nominated by any of the statutory bodies, to have access to inspect any aspect of its operations directly relating to the services and including the monitoring of quality assurance programmes as described in the schedules.

## 16 Assignment of Service Agreement

The unit will not assign any of its rights, benefits or obligations or delegate any of its responsibilities under this agreement without the prior consent in writing of the authority.

Where such consent is given, the unit is not released from any of its obligations and liabilities under this agreement.

## 17 Work Undertaken For Other Purchasers

Contracts with other purchasers should comply with these terms and conditions, and cannot provide for any conditions, such as preferential access, that could prove detrimental to the contract the unit has with this health authority.

The potential for establishing additional contracts with another purchaser over and above those existing on 1 April 19●●, and negotiated as a result of the unit's capacity to undertake additional work, must be agreed with the authority prior to an agreement being finalised.

## 18 Legislation

The unit will ensure that it and its employees and agents comply with all relevant legislation, codes of practice, and the authority's policies and procedures. It will be the authority's responsibility to ensure that units are fully advised on national legislation and the regional health authority and authority guidelines and policies.

## 19 Responsibility

The unit will be responsible on behalf of the authority for any liability or loss from any action, suit, or claim arising out of or in connection with any work carried out by or on behalf of the unit or those authorised to act on its behalf in relation to the provision of services covered by this agreement. Equally it will be responsible for any loss occasioned by action arising out of or in connection with the construction, maintenance, or use by the unit or those authorised to act on its behalf, of the works or services constructed, operated, or used by it or the plant, apparatus, or equipment installed in that connection.

## 20 Confidentiality

Both parties will ensure that records and returns containing information relating to individual patients are prepared and processed within consistent and sound operational and managerial practices.

Access to such records will be restricted to the parties to this agreement, who will both comply with the provisions of the *Data Protection Act* and its regulations as amended from time to time.

## 21 Staffing

The unit will employ adequate numbers of suitably qualified staff of the calibre, level of experience, and grades necessary to execute the agreement at all times. At the present time the authority regards the funded establishment as the baseline measurement of staff numbers. In the event of units being unable to employ sufficient numbers of staff due to difficulties in recruitment and retention, discussions will take place between the Authority and the Unit.

The unit will ensure that every person it employs is at all times properly and sufficiently trained and instructed with regard to all relevant provisions of the agreement and the services specified.

**END OF DOCUMENT 1**

# DOCUMENT 2

## Blankshire Health Authority

## Service Specification For Gynaecology Services in the Blankby General Hospital Catchment Area

## 1 Aims

The aim is to provide a comprehensive gynaecology service for females of all ages, for the assessment, investigation, provision of advice and treatment relating to the diseases and disorders of the reproductive system.

## 2 Objectives

2.1 To provide comprehensive gynaecological and related services that are safe, efficient, effective, appropriate, accessible, equitable, and acceptable to all sections of the community.

2.2 To provide elective and emergency services so that care is received without unreasonable delay.

2.3 To provide a personal service, sensitive to the physical, emotional and social needs of the consumers.

## 3 Population to be served and location of services

3.1 The population to be served is the resident female population in the Blankby General Hospital catchment area, with hospital in-patient and day-case services required at Blankby General Hospital. Out-patient services need to be provided at Blankby and Anytown.

3.2 The following population figures show the total estimated district resident population, the resident female population and current projections. Some broad estimation is also made of the Blankby General Hospital catchment area.

**POPULATION IN THOUSANDS: PROJECTED TO 1993**

|                  | 1988 | 1989 | 1990 | 1993 |
|------------------|------|------|------|------|
| District resident | 307  | 311  | 310  | 321  |
| District female   | 156  | 158  | 156  | 160  |
| Blankby female    | 39   | 40   | 39   | 40   |

## 4 Strategic direction

4.1 The authority sees no significant changes in volume or location of service provision – local access to consultant out-patient clinics continues to be important and must be maintained. Proposals for changes to the numbers and locations of out-patient clinics will be welcomed by the authority if they are shown to reflect need.

4.2 In general terms, the need to increase the amount of surgery undertaken on a day-case basis is a national, regional and authority objective, and the authority will liaise with provider units to decide how this can be achieved.

## 5 Elements of service to be provided

5.1 A comprehensive gynaecology service for the reception, assessment, treatment, and rehabilitation of those requiring emergency services. This includes, if required, in-patient admission at a district general hospital, and access to the existing range of diagnostic and clinical/non-clinical support services.

5.2 Consultant out-patient services at the locations listed at 3.1, with access to the existing range of diagnostic and clinical/non-clinical support services.

5.3 Elective in-patient and day-case services at Blankby General Hospital, with access to operating facilities, anaesthetic services and intensive care, together with the full range of currently available hospital diagnostic, rehabilitation and non-clinical support departments.

5.4 Domiciliary visits to patients for whom this is considered clinically/socially appropriate.

5.5 Colposcopy services undertaken on an out-patient or day-patient basis.

5.5 Arrangements for tertiary referrals to other centres, when considered to be in the interest of the patient, should be made by the provider unit. There will be separate arrangements made by the authority for contracting and payment to these other centres.

5.7 Facilities for pre- and post-registration training of nurses and any post-basic training for all staff considered necessary to maintain and develop expertise in the specialty.

5.8 Liaison with the community/mental health unit and other agencies to ensure effective discharge arrangements.

5.9 Any other supporting hospital services (or services provided by non-NHS bodies) required during an episode of care that are considered necessary by the clinician for the support and wellbeing of the patient.

## 6 Volume and activity

6.1 Completed consultant episodes for gynaecology at Blankby General Hospital for 1990/91 were 947 , and in 1991/92 were 909. Estimates for 1992/93 are 950, and for 1993/94 are 975. Day cases in 1990 were 141; in 1991/92 they were 132, and are estimated to rise to 150 in 1992/93, and to 160 in 1993/94. Out-patient attendances totalled 4077 in 1990/91, were 3730 in 1991/92, and are projected to be 3800 in 1992/93, and 3850 in 1993/94.

6.2 The estimates for 1992/93 in particular are based on past trends where these can be detected, and based on data that may not be wholly reliable. The authority regards these as maximum workloads that could be carried out and for which payment will be made, assuming that the indicative case-mix does not change significantly. Workload activity will be monitored through 1992/93 and the authority will discuss what action should be taken by providers if it appears that the maximum workload will be exceeded before the financial year end.

6.3 Activity data are based on referral patterns at that time, and whereas this agreement is principally concerned with securing services for residents in the Blankby General Hospital catchment area, it does not exclude residents from elsewhere in the district being treated if referral patterns change.

## 7 Type of contract

The authority will negotiate a block contract for the provision of gynaecological services in the Blankby General Hospital catchment area, based on indicative clinical activity with an upper limit and current case-mix. This will be reviewed after 12 months of operation, and assuming that information systems are sufficiently developed then a move towards a cost/volume or cost/volume and cost-per-case contract will be discussed with providers.

## 8 Quality issues

In addition to the general quality issues applicable to all contracts, providers must:

a) Produce a unit or departmental quality assurance strategy covering all aspects of gynaecological care. If this is not currently available then the provider should state when it will be.
b) Indicate how customer satisfaction will be measured and deficiencies remedied.
c) Have plans to provide continued training and education for all staff.
d) Advise the purchaser about proposals to develop medical audit so that all clinicians can participate.

e) Advise the purchaser about the outcomes against which the delivery of the service objectives will be monitored. The purchaser will work with the provider to develop these.

f) Show evidence that the delivery of nursing care given to all gynaecology patients is in accordance with the Standards for Nursing Services, as agreed by the District Nursing and Midwifery Advisory Committee.

g) Demonstrate that there is evidence that the prime focus of nursing care is on gynaecology patients and their carers (e.g. primary nursing, patient allocation, team nursing).

h) Care for terminally ill patients when it is not possible or appropriate for them to be cared for at home. All staff should be familiar with and carry out the 'hospice' approach to the care of the dying and their families, and should liaise with community staff to this end.

## 9 Standards

The authority regards the following standards as important and wishes the provider to achieve these (where they are not already being achieved) within proposals with a suggested timescale for implementation:

a) Increase day-case activity in selected procedures, e.g. legal termination of pregnancy or laparoscopic sterilisation, where current activity is well below what could be achieved.

b) No patient should wait for more than 1 year for non-urgent admission/treatment.

c) No patient should wait more than 6 weeks for an initial non-urgent out-patient appointment.

d) A booked admission system should operate for all patients, with 80% of all in-patients being given a firm admission date and 90% of out-patients being given a firm appointment date.

e) Waiting time in out-patient clinics should not exceed 30 minutes before the patient is seen by a member of the medical staff. Waiting time in other clinics or departments should not exceed 15 minutes before the patient is seen by the appropriate professional. If delays seem inevitable then patients must be told the reasons for delay and how long this will be.

f) All care should be provided in as homely and caring a setting as possible, upholding the dignity, privacy, and individual choice of the patient at all times.

g) A discharge summary should be sent at the time of discharge to the patient's general practitioner following an episode of in-patient or day-patient care, with a full report being sent within 1 week.

h) A named registered nurse should be accountable for the nursing care of each gynaecology patient.

i) A nursing care plan, based on a model of nursing, should be developed after an assessment of the patient by a registered nurse.

j) All patients should be seen by a consultant at the first (new) attendance at an out-patient clinic.

## 10 Monitoring and information requirements

10.1 The provider will need to submit information about the service to satisfy national and regional requirements, i.e. the minimum data set contained in the various statistical returns. These requirements are currently under review and the provider will be notified of these as soon as possible.

10.2 The authority will continue to have access to aggregated patient data and anonymised individual patient data contained on the regional patient information system and any other computer system which might replace this.

10.3 The following additional information will be required by the authority to monitor contracts and evaluate health needs:

● Quarterly – total patients waiting over 6 months for admission, by name/identifier and by site, with date on list and operation planned. Total admitted from waiting list and total added during quarter.
● Monthly – consultant episodes to show diagnoses and operative procedure, referring GP, postcode, patient's date-of-birth, duration of stay, and episode cost (if available).
● Quarterly – out-patient clinics, indicating those where patients wait for a first non-urgent appointment for more than 6 weeks, and total patients waiting.

## 11 Health outcome measures

11.1 As required – information resulting from the medical audit to be provided to the Director of Public Health.

11.2 As required – information relating to the outcomes of customer satisfaction surveys.

**END OF DOCUMENT 2**

# DOCUMENT 3

## Service Specification For Community Health

### between

### Blankshire District Health Authority

### and

### Blankby Directly Managed Unit

## 1 Aims
The aim is to provide a comprehensive integrated community health service for people of all ages in order to maximise their health potential and quality of life, and to ensure that care is provided in the community.

## 2 Objectives
2.1 To provide comprehensive community-based services which are safe, efficient, effective, appropriate, accessible and acceptable to all sections of the community.

2.2 To provide a personal service sensitive to the physical, emotional and social needs of the consumers, and in particular to the special needs of high-risk groups.

2.3 To provide a service that promotes and maintains the optimum health, wellbeing and independence of the population.

2.4 To develop clear and integrated planning and management arrangements between all the different agencies involved, whether statutory, private, or voluntary.

## 3 Population to be Served and Location of Services
3.1 The population to be served is the resident population of this district. Services should continue to be provided at the locations currently utilised, as listed on the attached service schedules. Should service demands at particular locations fall below a viable level of

operation, the unit will consult on any closure proposals in accordance with the authority's recognised procedures.

3.2 The following population figures show the total estimated district resident population, broken down by age bands, and the current projections.

| Total district resident population | Mid-1988 Estimate | 1989 Estimate | 1990 Projection | 1993 Projection |
|---|---|---|---|---|
| 0 – 4 | 17.6 | 18.0 | 19.3 | 22.0 |
| 5 – 14 | 36.3 | 36.4 | 34.6 | 35.8 |
| 15 – 64 | 200.8 | 203.4 | 204.9 | 211.3 |
| 65+ | 52.1 | 53.0 | 51.4 | 51.7 |
| Total population | 306.8 | 310.8 | 310.2 | 320.8 |

## 4 Strategic Direction

4.1 The authority recognises that the early discharge of patients, increased day-case treatment and changes in clinical practice place additional pressures on community services. The authority will wish to ensure that close cooperation and liaison between units is maintained, and the guidance given in HC(89)5 is followed.

4.2 The authority would welcome proposals for discussion in relation to the provision/development of a comprehensive community-based occupational therapy service.

4.3 The authority will wish to prepare with the provider unit a strategic plan for community health services.

## 5 Elements of the Service to be Provided

5.1 A Clinical Medical Officer service for children from birth to school-leaving, covering (Schedule 14 refers):

- Surveillance, screening, assessment, vaccination and immunisation, and health promotion.
- Advice to other agencies, most notably education and social services on adopting, fostering, child employment, and children with special educational needs.
- A limited range of occupational health services for the education department.

5.2 A district nursing service, to residents who require nursing support in their homes, and to the community, in order to improve and maximise the quality of life and the health potential of the population.

5.3 A health visiting service, to promote and maintain the optimum health, wellbeing and independence of the population.

5.4 A school nursing service, which provides health screening advice, prophylaxis and identification of emotional and social problems.

5.5 A child protection service, within the framework of the Area Child Protection Committee.

5.6 A community dental service, complementary to the hospital and general dental practitioner services, providing, in particular, preventative dental health education in children, provision of a comprehensive inspection and treatment service for pre-school and school children, specialist emergency services, orthodontic surveillance and treatment, assessment of epidemiological data, and monitoring of the effectiveness of preventive and treatment aspects of care.

5.7 A chiropody assessment and treatment service, available to those who have a demonstrable need for chiropody treatment and advice, supplemented by a programme of foot health education.

5.8 A speech therapy service, for assessment, treatment and education, and catering for the needs of children and adults with developmental or acquired communication disorders, including those affected by strokes, neurological disorders, head injuries, voice and fluency problems, the mentally and physically handicapped, those with special educational needs, the mentally ill and elderly, and patients with swallowing difficulties.

5.9 A community paediatric physiotherapy service, offering treatment to children who have any childhood condition, whether acute or chronic, that threatens physical development and may handicap their potential for adult independence.

5.10 A health promotion service that supports and facilitates changes in behaviour in order to promote healthy lifestyles and the initial prevention and early detection and reduction of disease amongst individuals and within communities.

5.11 Home loans and wheelchair services.

5.12 A family planning and advice service (including specialist services) complementary to that provided by general practitioners.

5.13 A cervical cytology service that complements general practitioner services.

5.14 An effective vaccination and immunisation programme complementary to that provided by general practitioners, in order to achieve an overall acceptance rate of 95% for all diseases.

5.15 An integrated palliative and bereavement care service to patients and their families in their homes.

5.16 A full range of clinical/non-clinical supporting services, either by direct provision or by purchase from other providers.

5.17 Professional advice to private nursing homes in the areas of MacMillan Nursing and Younger Disabled Services.

5.18 Facilities made available to the College of Nursing for the pre- and post-registration training of nurses.
5.19 Post-basic training for all staff considered necessary to maintain and develop expertise in the specialty.

## 6 Volume and Activity
Information on activity is shown in each of the service schedules (not enclosed in this sample).

## 7 Type of Contract
The authority will negotiate a block contract for the provision of district-wide community health services based on indicative clinical activity with an upper limit (see para. 6).

## 8 Quality Issues
In addition to the general quality issues applicable to all contracts, the provider must:

a) Produce a unit quality assurance strategy covering each aspect of community services. If this is not currently available, the provider should state when it will be.
b) Indicate how consumer satisfaction will be measured and deficiencies remedied.
c) Produce written guidance on the roles and responsibilities of staff in the unit, and keep this updated.
d) Have plans to provide continued training and education for all staff.
e) Advise the purchaser about proposals to develop medical audit so that all clinicians can participate.
f) Advise the purchaser about the outcomes against which the delivery of service objectives can be measured. The purchaser will work with the provider to develop these.
g) Show evidence that the delivery of nursing care given to all patients is in accordance with the *Standards for Nursing Services*, as agreed by the District Nursing and Midwifery Advisory Committee.
h) Demonstrate that there is evidence that the prime focus of nursing care is on the patients and their carers (e.g. primary nursing, patient allocation, team nursing).

## 9 Standards
The authority regards the following standards as important and wishes the provider to achieve these (where they are not already being achieved) within a timescale to be mutually agreed. The provider should submit draft proposals with a suggested timescale for achievement.

a) Reception, assessment, examination, and treatment facilities should be provided in an environment which is welcoming, comfortable, and encourages the confidence of the individual.

b   The dignity, privacy, and individual choice of the patient should be upheld at all times.
c)  No patient should wait more than 4 weeks for an initial non-urgent appointment, either in clinic premises or at home, other than where indicated in the attached schedules.
d)  Waiting times in clinics should not exceed 15 minutes from the appointment time before the patient is seen by a trained member of staff. If delays seem inevitable then patients must be told the reason for the delay and how long this will be.
e)  Information on the range of services available should be available to patients.
f)  Appointment times of day (am/pm) and date will normally be given for all home visits, with more specific times whenever possible.
g)  A named registered nurse should be accountable for the nursing care of each patient.
h)  A care plan, based on a model of nursing, should be developed after an assessment of the patient by a registered nurse.

## 10 Monitoring and Information Requirements

10.1 The provider will need to submit information about the service to satisfy national and regional requirements, i.e. the minimum data set contained in the various statistical returns. These requirements are currently under review and the provider will be notified of these as soon as possible.

10.2 The provider will need to further develop the child health computer system and provide access to the authority to anonymised individual and aggregated patient data.

10.3 The authority will wish to work with the provider to determine meaningful community-based information. In the meantime the following additional information will be required to monitor contracts and evaluate health needs:

● Quarterly – clinics or service areas indicating where patients have to wait for more than 6 weeks for a first, non-urgent appointment, and total numbers waiting.
● Annually – staffing information, numbers, staff groups, grades, and teaching undertaken.

# Index